NIKKEN®

To all our Nikken friends:

Buckle up, you're about to take a ride into the future. In this book, Paul Zane Pilzer shows you what the next 10 years will look like. It's a great vision for the Nikken Distributor.

Mr. Pilzer explains that the wave of the sickness industry has begun to break. People who used to spend so much money treating their illnesses are getting wiser. They're shifting that money and energy into staying healthy. They need and want products and services to keep them well, to keep them out of the doctors' offices.

Doesn't that sound great for the people who offer health and wellness technology?

Mr. Pilzer calls the wellness industry the next $1 trillion business. Nikken and its distributors are poised to fill this great need. You can be at the forefront of this movement. The stock market may be a gamble, but the wellness industry is a sure thing.

That huge population surge we call the Baby Boom is reaching an age when wellness is the #1 priority. Baby Boomers have the money and desire to fuel "The Next Trillion."

Get ready. It's coming. Enjoy the ride.

NIKKEN, INC.

Kendall Cho
President/COO

Also by Paul Zane Pilzer

Other People's Money
Unlimited Wealth
God Wants You To Be Rich

THE
NEXT
TRILLION

Why the wellness industry
will exceed the $1 trillion
healthcare (sickness) industry
in the next ten years

Paul Zane Pilzer

Prepublication Version

This is a Prepublication Version of *The Next Trillion*.
It is not for sale to the general public.

Nikken, Inc. Edition
Published by VideoPlus, Inc.
©2001 by ZCI, Inc.

VideoPlus is a registered trademark of VideoPlus, Inc., Dallas, TX

Designed by Stephanie Elieff

Printed in the United States of America

To J. I. Rodale, 1898–1971

Table of Contents

page

i   Preface: We Have Met the Enemy
    and He Is Us!

1   Introduction: Today's Heresy Is
    Tomorrow's Dogma

5   Chapter One: Your Money and Your Life

21 Chapter Two: God Wants You To Be Healthy

33 Chapter Three: The Next Trillion

43 Chapter Four: Demand

59 Chapter Five: Distribution

81 Chapter Six: Sickness Insurance

97 Chapter Seven: Paying for Wellness

125 Chapter Eight: Epilogue

137 Appendix 1: Food—An Economic Perspective

153 Appendix 2: Fat—What Is It, and How Much
    Is Too Much?

159 Appendix 3: Highlights from *The Next Trillion*

177 Selected Bibliography

183 Index

189 Acknowledgments

196 About the Author

Preface

We Have Met the Enemy and He Is Us!

Most of the college students I teach today were born after the Vietnam War ended. Having always lived in such peaceful times, they cannot comprehend the depth of the tragedy we have created.

Economically we live in halcyon days that have far surpassed the wildest dreams of our forebears, who fought so hard and lost so much to create what we have today.

And yet, we begin this millennium with more human unhappiness than at any time in our history.

America is, as Disraeli once said of England, "two nations" divided by great want. More than half the U.S. population is not enjoying the fruits of this great economy, and this division is not because of their annual income, the color of their skin, their religion, or the place where they were born.

Fully 61 percent of Americans are trapped within their own prison of being overweight and in ill-health, and almost half of those, about 27 percent, are clinically obese—overweight to a point where they are hopeless and have no idea where to turn for help.

Moreover, a similar situation exists in Western Europe, Japan and most other developed nations.

There is no "Great Satan" to blame for our current situation. As a society, to quote the words of a popular comic strip, "We have met the enemy and he is us."[1] But as individuals, whether we desire to help ourselves or someone we love, there is much that we can do.

Paul Zane Pilzer, Park City, Utah

---

[1] Kelly, Walter, "The Pogo Papers," 1952–1953. Walt Kelly also used this quote on a poster for Earth Day in 1970 (http://www.igopogo.com).

Introduction

Today's Heresy Is Tomorrow's Dogma

In 1954, entrepreneur and author J. I. Rodale had a lot to lose. His company, Rodale Press, was just getting his fledgling *Prevention* magazine off the ground. *Prevention* was dedicated to teaching readers how to prevent disease versus just treating the symptoms of disease.

J.I. had concluded, after studying all the available scientific data, that eating large quantities of red meat and dairy products dramatically increased the risk of heart disease, and that physical activity actually decreased the risk of having a heart attack. But this was at a time when the U.S. government was spending millions encouraging Americans to eat more red meat and dairy products at every meal, three meals a day. And doctors were telling patients with heart disease to reduce or eliminate physical activity entirely. No wonder heart disease was the leading cause of death in America!

Rodale wrote about his new findings in two books: *How to Eat for a Healthy Heart* and *This Pace Is Not Killing Us*. He was convinced that this information could save millions of lives. But, like many writers in the 1950s, he was not on an "approved list" drawn up by Senator Joseph McCarthy's House Un-American Activities Committee, so the large New York publishers refused to publish his new books.

This situation forced Rodale to print the books himself and try to sell them through bookstores along with his other Rodale publications. But many booksellers also refused to distribute his new books. Undaunted and convinced that the public needed this information as soon as possible, J.I. took full-page advertisements in national publications and offered his new books together via mail order at a special price.

The Federal Trade Commission ordered Rodale to stop advertising and selling the books, claiming that the medical advice given in his books was unsubstantiated. The FTC had successfully taken similar action against other publishers who had promulgated then-unconventional medical advice.[2]

Rodale was furious! He felt that the FTC action was a blatant violation of the First Amendment guaranteeing freedom of the press.

The FTC scheduled hearings in 1955 in which Rodale was ordered to present proof that people who purchased the books and followed their advice would, indeed, reduce their risk of heart disease. Rodale refused to attend, claiming that the First Amendment gave him the right to publish any information he wanted—regardless of its efficacy.[3]

---

[2]Witkower Press, Inc., of Hartford, Connecticut, had published a book *Arthritis and Common Sense* and claimed in their advertisements that it would help arthritic and rheumatoid sufferers. In 1954 the FTC ordered the Witkower Press to "forthwith cease and desist from representing, directly or indirectly, that their book was adequate, effective, and reliable in giving relief to arthritic and rheumatoid sufferers." Witkower Press accepted the ruling and did not appeal the case. In a similar case against Prentice Hall, the large publisher agreed to the FTC action because they did not want to enter into costly litigation with the federal government. (Pilzer, Paul Zane, "Rodale Press versus The Federal Trade Commission: A Comprehensive Analysis," Senior Thesis, Lehigh University, Bethlehem, PA, May 21, 1974.)

[3]At the original hearing on this case before the FTC examiner, dissenting FTC commissioner Elman foreshadowed the path that the FTC was about to take when he wrote: "Congress did not create this Commission to act as a censor of unorthodox ideas and theories in books, whether they deal with politics or health.

At these hearings, the nation's most respected medical professionals testified that: (1) there was no correlation between heart disease and eating large quantities of red meat and dairy products; and (2) following Rodale's advice on increasing physical activity to avoid heart disease could be injurious, if not fatal. The FTC ordered Rodale to "cease and desist" from claiming, directly or indirectly, that readers of any of his publications would improve their health.[4] Rodale appealed the case, mainly on the grounds that the First Amendment prohibited the FTC from regulating information-based products. His legal battles with the federal government dragged on for more than a decade, at times putting his entire personal net worth at risk.

Over the years, the FTC feared at times that they would lose their case on constitutional grounds and attempted to settle with Rodale. But despite financial hardship, Rodale refused to back down unless the FTC agreed to acknowledge that the First Amendment prohibited them from regulating books and printed material. The FTC refused.

During the 1960s, as the case dragged on through the U.S. courts, Rodale's attorney, Abe Fortas, had to withdraw when Fortas was appointed as a Justice of the Supreme Court of the United States. Fortas's law partner Thurman Arnold took on the case.

We should not forget that, in both fields, today's heresy may become tomorrow's dogma." (Ibid.)

[4]FTC Commissioner Philip Elman, a Kennedy appointee and former law clerk to Supreme Court Justice Felix Frankfurter, wrote in his dissenting opinion: "It is the glory of a free society that a man can write a book contending that the earth is flat, or that the moon is made of green cheese, or that God is dead, without having to 'substantiate' or 'prove' his claims to the satisfaction of some public official or agency. . . . It is arrogance to presume that in any field of knowledge, whether dealing with health or otherwise, all the answers are now in." (Ibid.)

Thurman Arnold introduced new testimony from
some of the same leading medical experts that the
government originally used at the initial FTC
hearings 15 years earlier. One by one these "experts"
refuted their original testimony, claiming they "didn't
know back then," and admitted that over the years
many of Rodale's original claims had become
established medical facts. Arnold felt that there could
never be a better example of what our Founding
Fathers had in mind when they made freedom of the
press the very first item in the Bill of Rights.

Then, in 1971, while describing his legal problems
with the federal government on national television, J.
I. Rodale dropped dead. Until he actually stopped
breathing and turned blue, everyone watching *The
Dick Cavett Show* thought that J.I. was facetiously
faking a heart attack in order to make a point about
his troubles with the FTC.

The case never reached the Supreme Court. But
soon after J.I.'s death, the FTC promulgated a new
policy stating that they would no longer require
advertisers of information-based products to
establish the efficacy of their claims. Perhaps more
than any other single action by the U.S. government,
this policy allowed the vitamin, nutritional
supplement, fitness and alternative medicine
industries to grow to the level they are today.

This pioneering, brave action by one man, who
risked everything in standing up to the federal
government for what he believed, paved the way for
the revolution in food and in healthcare that is about
to take place.

*Prevention magazine currently has 12 million
readers and Rodale Press (i.e., Men's Health, Runner's
World) is now the largest health-oriented publisher in
the world. Its book division freely publishes over 100
new titles each year that sell a combined total of 20
million copies per annum.*

Chapter 1

Your Money and Your Life

For the drunkard and the glutton shall come to poverty: and drowsiness shall clothe a man with rags.

Proverbs 23:21 (King James Bible)

It was September 7, 1996, at the RCA Dome in Indianapolis. I was getting ready to go onstage as the keynote speaker before 45,000 people. My speaking fee had just been given to me in a sealed envelope—more money for giving a 45-minute speech than I used to make in a full year working at Citibank.

I should have been elated. But instead I felt guilty. As I watched the audience file into the stadium, I felt as if I were about to rip them off.

Like most of America, half of the audience was unhealthy and overweight, a direct consequence of diet and lifestyle evidenced by the fatigued look on their faces and the fat hanging over their waistlines. For many of them, nothing I was about to say about economics was going to improve the quality of their lives until they first learned how to care for their bodies.

A strange urge seized me to scrap my prepared speech and tell my audience that good health was more important than any riches they might acquire, but I chickened out. I didn't want to offend my hosts. And truthfully, I didn't know back then what action most people should take in order to take control of their health. On the flight home the next morning I began to wrestle with this question: Why would intelligent people spend time and money to improve their lives in every area except the most obvious area in which they needed improvement. And, more significant, what should a person who is overweight and unhealthy do to begin taking control of his or her life.

As I began my research, I became excited about why an economist needed to write a book on the subject of food and diet.

I quickly discovered that the major reason so many people were unhealthy and obese had more to do with economics than with medicine—because there were incredibly powerful economic forces preventing people from taking control of their health and actually encouraging them to gain weight. Indeed, it may even be impossible for some people to take control of their health until they first understand the food and medical industries that represent 30 percent of our national economy.

I also discovered that the effects of obesity and poor health go far beyond just a person's appearance. In our new millennium we have replaced racial and gender discrimination with a new kind of discrimination based on a person's weight and appearance. Whereas in the past poverty was associated with thinness and obesity with wealth, most people who are overweight today occupy the lower rungs of the economic ladder.

Rich fat man has become an oxymoron, and *poor* and *fat* have become synonyms.

And incredibly, despite the fact that we are enjoying the greatest economic prosperity ever known to mankind, 61 percent of the U.S. population is overweight, and an incredible 27 percent are clinically obese. Both of these figures increased 10 percent from just 1994–1999, and obesity has almost doubled since the 1970s.[5]

---

[5]*Prevalence of Overweight and Obesity Among Adults: United States, 1999*, National Center for Health Statistics, Centers for Disease Control (CDC).

Weight and appearance now define social and economic opportunities just as family name and birth did in the nineteenth century. When a person is fat—not just 15 pounds overweight but clinically obese—it is hard to find a job, a relationship, or the energy to stay on top of the everyday demands of even a simple life.

Even most people with normal weight are unhealthy, although they often don't know it. Modern medicine tells them to accept headaches, body pain, fatigue, arthritis, and thousands of other common ailments as inevitable symptoms that afflict an aging population. Yet these ailments, like being overweight and obesity, are the direct result of having a terrible diet.

Economics is largely to blame for this state of affairs. A powerful trillion-dollar food industry bombards us with messages calculated to make us eat more and more of the worst possible food. Understanding how the food industry works today is crucial for those seeking to control their diet and, ultimately, their life.

Packaged food companies, such as General Foods and Procter & Gamble, employ some of the best and brightest minds to study customer psychology and demographics. In trying to decide what sorts of foods to sell us, they invariably apply one of the great unwritten laws of marketing: It is easier to sell more product to an existing customer than to sell that same product to a new customer. In other words, it is easier to influence a regular customer to eat four additional bags of potato chips per month than it is to persuade a new customer, who may never have tasted potato chips before, to buy even one bag of this exotic new substance.

Most processed food sales, products like Hostess Twinkies, Oreo Cookies and McDonald's Happy Meals,[6] are governed by what those in the business call a "potato chip marketing equation." According to this law, more than 90 percent of product sales are made to less than 10 percent of their customers. In the case of processed foods, that coveted 10 percent consists largely of people weighing more than 200 pounds and earning less than $20,000 per year.

Each company studies its 10 percent, people known as the "target market," like rats in a laboratory. Customer surveys reveal their likes, dislikes, hopes, dreams, heroes and desires. High-consumption customers are recruited to take part in focus groups, where they are asked to sample new products, view advertising and offer opinions.

No expense is spared to hit every psychological button that matters to the target market. If people in that market like a particular actor or singer, that very celebrity will soon appear on radio or television, praising the product. If a certain look, feel, or lifestyle appeals to people in that market, legions of stylists and designers will descend on the studio to simulate it. Like a deer caught in the telescopic sight of a hunter at close range, the target never has a chance.

Such ruthless tactics used to be restricted to U.S. tobacco companies, which wrote the book on deceptive marketing tactics while getting the world addicted to nicotine. Recent legislation has forced Big Tobacco to curb some of these activities when it comes to promoting cigarettes, especially to children. But, unfortunately, they are not letting their acquired expertise go to waste—they are purchasing the major brands of addictive processed foods. In early 2001 Philip Morris, the world's largest tobacco company, purchased some of the most popular children's processed food brands, including Oreo Cookies, Ritz

---

[6]Hostess Twinkies, Oreo Cookies, and McDonald's Happy Meals are registered trademarks respectively of the Interstate Bakeries Corporation, Nabisco, Inc., and McDonald's Corporation.

Crackers and Life Savers candies.[7] This makes Philip Morris the world's second largest food company after Nestle, Inc.[8]

At times, the ruthlessness of the process troubles the consciences of the $200,000-per-year marketing executives in charge of it. Some actually refuse to attend the focus groups. Rather than confront their future victims in person, they prefer to review transcripts in the safety of their offices. Imagine what table talk must be like in the homes of such executives. "Today, I met ten 200-pound women who barely had the energy to participate in the group," they'd report to their families over dinner. "If my team can get each of them up to 210 pounds by April by increasing their consumption of our potato chips, we'll make our first-quarter numbers and I'll get the bonus we need to take that vacation in Barbados."

The executive himself is probably eating a healthy meal, even as he speaks these words.

One of the great scandals of the junk-food culture is the extent to which its most enthusiastic promoters personally avoid the very products they are pushing. Moreover, many of the emotional and medical challenges some people face today, from controlling one's temper to depression and cancer, are as much products of these junk-food companies as are frozen pizza and "low-fat" cookies.

As my research took me to the medical industry, I encountered large multinational companies whose nefarious practices made those of the food companies

---

[7]Oreo Cookies, Ritz Crackers, and Life Savers candies are trademarks of Nabisco Holdings, Inc.

[8]On December 6, 2000 the Federal Trade Commission approved the sale of Nabisco Holdings Corp. to Philip Morris Cos., Inc. Nabisco Holdings makes Oreo Cookies, Ritz Crackers, and Life Savers candies. ("FTC Approves Nabisco-Philip Morris Deal," *New York Times,* December 7, 2000).

pale by comparison. It quickly became apparent to me why an economist needed to write about obtaining good medical care along with how to obtain food for a healthy lifestyle.

When a patient goes to see a physician, he or she believes they are receiving a prescription for the best drug or treatment available for their specific ailment. Not likely.

Just as obese consumers represent the "target" market to the food companies, physicians represent the "target" market to the medical and pharmaceutical companies. The patient receives the drug or treatment that is most profitable for the supplier of the treatment, the health insurance company, and in some cases even the individual physician. This may or may not represent the best medical treatment available. In the United States, doctors typically prescribe completely different treatments for the same ailment depending on which drug company has the dominant market share in their region.

Medical technology and pharmaceuticals change so fast today that what physicians learn in medical school is often obsolete by the time they graduate. In practice, doctors learn about new drugs and treatments from a special type of salesperson called a "detail person" in the medical industry. "Detail person" is actually a euphemism for "a very attractive, highly paid young person of the opposite sex." Detail people lavishly hand out free samples and handsomely reward physicians and their staff in proportion to the amount of prescriptions they write for their company's product. Physicians and their families receive expensive dinners and get cruises and tax-free trips to destination resorts where they "learn" more about such products at taxpayers' expense.

Although the ethical (prescription) pharmaceutical companies around the world justify the very high prices of their drugs with the high cost of research and development, drug companies actually spend much more money marketing their drugs than they do on research and development. Moreover, a considerable amount of the research and development that leads to the creation of new drugs is funded by the federal government through grants to nonprofit entities like research labs at universities and medical schools or by the National Institutes of Health.

When you pay the staggering prices for prescription drugs, you are also paying for the marketing campaign that successfully got the doctor to check the box on the prescription form that reads "DAW"—Dispense as Written. That means the prescription will be filled by the more expensive name brand rather than the cheaper generic, which is available for about ninety percent of all prescriptions. Most drug company profits come from often-outdated name-brand drugs taken by patients on an ongoing basis that were prescribed years ago when the patient first developed the condition. Prescription drug companies limit informing customers and physicians of improved products in cases where they might lose existing customers to competitive brands when the patient visits the doctor for their revised prescription. Generic drugs are often safer or better than the name-brand products they replace because they have been formulated or prescribed more recently.

In recent years the pharmaceutical companies have even hired the same advertising firms as the food companies and have begun direct image-based advertising to consumers. In these advertisements for prescription-only items that must legally be dispensed only upon the written recommendation of a doctor, the patient is directly sold on the product and told to "ask their doctor" for a DAW prescription—with the knowledge that if the doctor refuses to write the prescription, the presold patient will simply find another doctor who will.

Sadly, most physicians have become "technology dispensers" for the products and services of the large multinational medical companies—companies which always seem to tip the scale between profits and patients in favor of profits. In some cases this means manipulating the federal government against the public interest in safety as well as in dollars.

For example, Claritin® is the world's bestselling antihistamine for allergies. It is praised by the 50 million people who suffer from allergies in the United States—especially truckers and other long-distance drivers, because it alone does not cause drowsiness like its sedating-antihistamine competitors. Yet in the United States the manufacturer has manipulated the FDA to keep Claritin a prescription item in order to keep its U.S. price four times higher than the price charged for the exact same drug in other industrialized countries. This massive price difference ($62 for Claritin versus $4.50 for an over-the-counter sedating-antihistamine like Benadryl®) has resulted in 56 percent of U.S. allergy-sufferers using sedating (versus non-sedating) products.

According to the newspaper *USA Today,* this action by Claritin's manufacturer directly leads to 600 U.S. auto fatalities per year and to 47,740 injuries per year in antihistamine-related crashes. Incredibly, Claritin's manufacturer actually utilizes this same fatality and injury information overseas to promote sales of "safe," non-sedating, over-the-counter Claritin, while in the United States it lobbies the FDA to keep the drug a "controlled" prescription item in order to protect its $2.3 billion in domestic sales at the massively higher price.[9]

---

[9]"Allergy Drugs Remain Restricted," *USA Today,* 12 April 2000, 1.

These and so many other practices have pushed the price for U.S. drugs so high that patients cannot afford to fill approximately 22 percent of the prescriptions written each year. Prescription drugs now represent the single largest monthly expense for most over-65 U.S. citizens, approximately $300 per month, and millions of people sadly make the terrible choice today between purchasing their food or their medicine. Medicare pays for doctor visits but generally does not pay for prescriptions.[10]

But this and hundreds of other examples are just symptoms of some of the underlying problems with medical care in the developed world today—which are also almost all economic rather than scientific concerns.

One underlying problem is that it is more profitable for medical suppliers to produce products consumers use for the rest of their lives, rather than to make products that a consumer might use only once. Invariably, *this means spending research and development funds on products that treat the symptoms of diseases rather than the causes or the cures.*

Another underlying problem is that approximately 85 percent of Americans finance their medical care through a health insurance system where individuals bear no direct responsibility for their medical expenses, and where almost all expenses to prevent illness (e.g., exercise, vitamins, nutritional supplements) are disallowed for reimbursement. The American health insurance system is really a disguised payment and discounting mechanism

---

[10]Approximately 34 of 39 million patients on Medicare do not receive prescription drug coverage. Generally, the five million Medicare recipients receiving prescription drug coverage do so because they elected to receive a lower-standard of managed care in return for such prescription coverage.

designed to extract the most out of those who can often afford the least.

We will examine these and other underlying problems with medical care today. We will see an insurance system on the verge of collapse and will show how individuals can safeguard their families through the dangerous times ahead. And we will show how healthy individuals can opt out now of the employer-sponsored insurance system—saving themselves thousands of dollars each year with a tax-advantaged insurance program that covers wellness as well as sickness expenses.

While there is obviously no direct conspiracy between the $1 trillion food industry (which causes most of the problems) and the $1.4 trillion medical industry (that treats just enough of the symptoms to get the "targets" back to work and consumption), the economic effect is the same as if these two industries were conspiring against the American consumer in the most sinister fashion.

On a microeconomic level, each time consumers get real information that could help them take control of their health, the food and medical industries, acting in their own economic self-interest, manipulate this information against them.

For example, prior to 1990, consumers were told that simply eating too many calories caused obesity. When the public became aware that the amount of fat in their diets was a major cause of obesity, the food industry reacted with enticing low- and nonfat foods, advertising that consumers could now eat as much as they want without gaining weight. The food industry even repackaged many products that never had fat in them, like sugar-coated candies and pretzels, to suggest that they had created new healthy "nonfat" versions of these products.

What their massive advertising didn't tell consumers was that these low- and nonfat products

had terribly high levels of sugar and carbohydrates—
which turn to fat once ingested in the body—not to
mention addictive chemicals that made them worse
in the long run than the "fattening" products they
replaced. Throughout the 1990s obesity, as well as
the sales of low- and nonfat foods, steadily increased.

On a macroeconomic level it can also seem as if
there is no escape. When it comes to attempting to
control our federal, state and local governments, the
food and medical companies follow their own Golden
Rule: He with the gold makes the rules.

Lobbyists for the food industries have created
mandatory school lunch and milk programs that
hook children on addictive processed foods.
Pharmaceutical companies have helped create
government-sponsored programs that put millions of
children on dangerous drugs to combat the effects of
their terrible diets. In some cases, such as when
Ritalin is used to control hyperactive children,
parents are threatened with losing custody of their
own children if they refuse to force them to take such
drugs for alleged disorders.[11]

The U.S. Food and Drug Administration,
originally designed to protect consumers from
unhealthy products, now often protects the very
companies it is supposed to regulate by keeping out
competition and prolonging the economic life of the
drug companies' government-sanctioned patents.

Typically the news media, acting in its own self-
interest for publicity and ratings, leads society in
exposing such heinous activities. But in this case the
media is all too often ineffective. As consumers
themselves, the members of the media are subject to
the same disinformation and thus unaware of the

---

[11]Diller, Lawrence H., M.D., "Just Say Yes to Ritalin! Parents Are
Being Pressured by Schools to Medicate Their Kids—or Else,"
New York Times, September 24, 2000.

problem. And secondly, a major funding source for the media—especially network television advertising revenue—comes from food and drug companies.

For example, the detrimental health effect of drinking cow milk has been widely known for years in the medical community, but has rarely been covered by the media, which reaps fortunes each year running ads for the American Dairy Association—let alone the scandal of the celebrities who sport milk mustaches in paid advertisements but themselves only drink soy-based milk products.

The scandal of these celebrities goes even deeper than just endorsing products that they would never consume themselves. Leading actors, singers and models literally make millions of dollars each year on their looks. Most of them consume a pro-vegetarian diet lacking in processed and addictive fast foods. Yet these societal role models for fitness and beauty are cautioned by their managers not to let their elite dining habits become known to the press, lest they be boycotted by television producers in an industry where most of the revenue comes from advertisements for processed foods and fast-food restaurants.

Despite the fact that many young people admire them for more than just their professional talents, celebrities today have learned not to take positions on controversial issues that could affect their careers. As one celebrity manager once told me, no one wants to become the "Jane Fonda of healthy eating"—referring to the talented actress who was boycotted by some theatergoers in the 1970s because of her controversial left-wing political views.[12]

---

[12]One notable exception is the talented Alicia Silverstone—born 10/4/76, star of *Clueless* (1995), *Batman & Robin* (1997), and 13 other major films. While there are many famous vegetarian actors, including Brad Pitt, Kim Basinger, Richard Gere, Alec

In a free enterprise system, when people want something that can't be provided by profit-seeking entities, they typically turn to government ("the provider of last resort") for assistance. This worked well in the 1970s, when consumers demanded that government restrict the actions of businesses that were destroying the environment.

But in this case, government also seems helpless. Like the media, as consumers themselves, our elected officials are subject to the same disinformation and thus unaware of the problem. Take a look at the waistlines and the diets of most politicians if you want to know what they think of food and health! But more seriously, our politicians have been effectively controlled by the food and drug companies for so long that our government is now a large part of the problem rather than poised to be part of a solution.

Today we live at a time where we have won the Cold War, when democratic ideals are almost universally cherished from Moscow to Peking. Yet we also live at a time when half of our people have become personally enslaved—enslaved to a lifestyle that limits their daily lives, dreams and happiness as much as any authoritative government or dictatorship. Although it is not a conspiracy in the sense that it is ruled by a single individual or clique, it acts as if it were controlled by a single despot. The thousands of companies that comprise the United States' $1 trillion food industry and the $1.4 trillion medical industry are governed by universal laws of economics that cause them to act, in concert, as if

---

Baldwin, Drew Barrymore, Paul Newman, Liv Tyler, William Shatner, David Duchovny, Daryl Hannah, and Dustin Hoffman, to the detriment of her career Ms. Silverstone consistently uses her celebrity against the dairy and processed food lobbies in trying to teach healthy eating to her young fans.

they were part of a vast nefarious conspiracy.

Because of the economics that drive the food production industry, and the inability of the government to address the problem, U.S. obesity has almost doubled in the past two decades—from roughly 15 percent in 1980 to 27 percent today. Take a moment and think again of this figure in terms of human suffering—77 million Americans are now clinically obese, and 184 million are overweight and unhealthy because they lack the resources, information and motivation to safeguard their most precious asset: their wellness.

But, 39 percent of Americans are not overweight. America has become a healthocracy—a two-party system of "haves" and "have-nots"—divided between those who successfully manage their health and the health of their families and those who don't.

And within this 39 percent, there are millions of Americans who are eating and living healthier than ever before in history. This wellness-based group includes most of the movers and shakers in our society along with celebrities who, as noted earlier, literally make their living on how they look. *This group has quietly embraced a revolutionary new approach—to diet, to exercise, to vitamins, to nutritional supplements, to medical care, and, most important, to the aging process itself.*[13]

As we examine this fortunate group, we will see the beginnings of a new industry—an industry dedicated to wellness that will eventually far surpass the existing healthcare industry we have today that is

---

[13]If you want a more visual example, just watch the national evening news and notice the immediate difference between the people doing the reporting versus the "normal" people being reported on. Or watch MTV and notice the difference between the VJs and stars versus the occasional "fans" quoted for their comments.

dedicated to sickness.

The majority of the people reading this book are in this elite wellness-based group. At times, I feel like a minister who has written a sermon that he knows can turn around the lives of certain people, but who sadly knows that these certain people are not attending his, or any other, church.

But, I have written this book with great hope. I hope that my wellness-based readers will see this as a call to action—a call to action to share actively what they know with their friends, their neighbors and families. Every one of us personally knows someone who is not making it today because of his or her weight or health. Medical science has focused for too long on simply preserving the length of life without focusing on the quality of that life.

Take a moment now and think of people close to you who are unhealthy or overweight. Imagine how significantly their lives could change if they lost 15 pounds next month, or found the energy to enjoy their family at home after a full day of work, or had the pain they have been told to accept as they get older removed from their body.

Chapter 2

God Wants You To Be Healthy

Since by keeping the body in health and vigor one walks in the ways of God—it being impossible during sickness to have any understanding or knowledge of the Creator—it is a man's duty to avoid whatever is injurious to the body, and cultivate habits conducive to health and vigor.
       Moses Maimonides (1136-1204), Mishnah Torah

Most of the world's great religions originally succeeded because they addressed the secular along with the spiritual needs of their congregants. From the Israelites accepting the Ten Commandments and the Mosaic Code, to the Romans adopting the principles of Jesus Christ in 324 A.D., people followed religious laws, which then dealt mostly with secular issues, because they received a better life in the present separately from what they were being promised in the hereafter.

Over time the Judeo-Christian-Islamic principles for how human beings should treat one another evolved into the secular law of the land for everyone (e.g., the *U.S. Constitution*).

Then, when it came to human behavior, religion shifted its focus toward (1) teaching people the right personal choices to make for a better life; and (2) giving people the strength through faith to be able to make these choices.[14]

---

[14]Whereas the Ten Commandments (ca. 2000 B.C.) dealt mostly with laws and prescribed punishments by man, the monastic seven deadly sins written 2,500 years later deal entirely with human behavioral issues outside the purview of government regulation.

The ability to make such choices is what separates us from the animal kingdom. Humans and animals have virtually the same pleasurable biological desires when it comes to eating food, elimination, sex, etc. with one all-important difference: Humans have a mind and soul that can be taught to be superior to their biological desires.[15]

Today, when it is technically legal to commit adultery, lie, and engage in unethical business behavior, as well as countless other activities that could destroy the value of our lives, it is our religious principles that guide us to make the right choices— choices that often mean rejecting immediate gratification in return for a greater long-term benefit. Yet one of the most important choices we make today, what and how we eat, has escaped the purview of most modern religions.

Gluttony is denounced from Exodus through Jude, and is one of the seven deadly sins in early Christianity.[16] The New Testament even predicts that gluttons will become poor (Proverbs 23:21).

---

[15]This superiority is not innate. When an infant wants to eliminate, it does, getting a short-term benefit: the pleasure from elimination. Over time infants learn how to limit where and when they eliminate in favor of a longer-term benefit: keeping their bodies and households clean. As infants become children, such conscious decisions to forgo pleasure now in favor of greater pleasure tomorrow apply to everything else in their lives (e.g., learning to control anger, studying, choosing friends). I believe that the more we learn how to make such conscious, thoughtful decisions, the closer we become to God.

[16]The traditional catalog of the seven deadly sins is: (1) vainglory, or pride; (2) covetousness; (3) lust, understood as inordinate or illicit sexual desire; (4) envy; (5) gluttony, which usually included drunkenness; (6) anger; and (7) sloth. They were identified during the early history of Christian monasticism and grouped together in the sixth century by St. Gregory the Great. (Merriam-Webster's Encyclopedia of Literature, ©1996 Zane Publishing, Inc. and Merriam-Webster, Inc.)

Yet today, when 61 percent of our population is overweight, gluttony is virtually ignored by most religions and religious organizations. Even those religions that focus heavily on diet, such as Orthodox Judaism and Islam, are missing this all-important issue by focusing on archaic laws of cleanliness (e.g., eating kosher) versus the true dietary needs of most of their congregants (e.g., diet, vitamins, minerals and avoiding obesity).

One of the reasons for this paradox is that many of the world's major religions were founded at a time of agricultural scarcity: They have not caught up with technological advances that have shifted our major dietary issues from the problems of starvation and cleanliness to the problems of overeating and voluntary malnutrition.

Today, in most developed nations, where food is ubiquitous, religious people begin meals with prayers thanking God for providing them food, and children are told to finish everything on their plates. Prayers in these nations should thank God for giving them the knowledge of what to eat, or thank God for the family and friends with whom they are about to dine. Children should be taught to eat only when their stomach tells them that their body needs nourishment, not when their taste buds tell them they want immediate gratification. Obesity among children is rising even faster than obesity in adults.

Another reason this paradox exists is ignorance. Our religious leaders are simply unaware of what to eat for a healthy life due to the level of disinformation on food and health in the marketplace. One of the ways the great religions of the world became widespread was by addressing social injustice and the secular needs of their congregants: Today there is perhaps no greater social injustice, and no greater secular need, than the need of their congregants to take responsibility for and control of their weight and health.

When it comes to inspiring people to be able to make the right choices for a better life, faith is the highest motivating force in the world—faith in a higher power and faith in a higher purpose than just being enslaved by our biological drives. More than 95 percent of the people in the United States believe in God, and more than 60 percent attend regularly scheduled religious services.

The right choices to make on food and health can be traced back to the original teachings of Moses, Jesus, Mohammed and their disciples. The concept of getting close to God through having a fit and healthy body is evident throughout the Old and New Testaments, but became purged in the Middle Ages as a reaction to the emphasis placed on physical appearance and beauty by Greek and Roman persecutors. Yet, a careful rereading of the founding documents of these world religions clearly demonstrates that *God wants us to be healthy.* The most common book of the bible to three major religions, Genesis, speaks of the Garden of Eden, where God made "every tree that is pleasant to the sight, and good for food."[17] This reference to a wide variety of food has more than just aesthetic significance.

In addition to requiring food for chemical energy, the human body requires a daily intake of 13 essential vitamins[18]—most of which the body cannot manufacture on its own. These vitamins, along with certain minerals, are necessary to sustain the

---

[17]Genesis 2:9 (King James Bible)

[18]The term "vitamin" was coined in 1912 by biochemist Casimir Funk. Funk discovered that these substances were "vital" for life and he originally thought that they were all ammonia-based products—hence the term "vital amine" or "vitamin." Later, as scientists identified the critical 13 vitamins required for human life they discovered they were not all ammonia-based substances.

millions of chemical reactions our bodies perform each day. Eating the proper variety of fresh fruits and vegetables throughout the day gives us all of what we need.

The majority of Americans, however, including many who appear healthy on the outside, are not getting the minimal amount of these vitamins and minerals that their bodies require.

Over the short term these deficiencies manifest themselves as a lack of energy, joint pain, failing eyesight, hearing loss and thousands of other ailments that medical science tells us to accept with advancing age. Over the long term these deficiencies cause major illnesses like cancer and heart disease.[19]

In addition to the vitamins and minerals required for human life and development, there are many natural supplements that are highly effective in treating ailments that afflict everyone at some point in their lives. These age-old natural remedies—from gingko to improve our memories to St. John's wort to alleviate depression—continually illuminate the famous Kabbalistic statement: *"God creates the cure before he sends the malady" (Zohar, twelfth century).*[20]

Many people arrogantly think we live in some great age of universal scientific knowledge. But when it comes to nutrition, vitamins, minerals, and natural supplements and how they support the immune system to prevent disease and affect the aging process, we are largely only where medical science

---

[19]See Appendix 1. One of the reasons for these deficiencies is that few Americans find the time to eat the proper variety of foods. Another reason is that the more we process foods from their natural state—mostly to differentiate them as distinct brands and to retard spoilage—the less efficacious their vitamins become. In addition, some vitamins should be taken with certain foods in order to be digested correctly.

[20]Zohar I, 196A.

was two centuries ago when it came to conquering infectious disease.

Prior to the nineteenth century, doctors administered the few medicines that existed, and by way of trial-and-error observed which medicines cured which diseases. Medical knowledge was accumulated like this over centuries and occasionally diffused between cultures.[21]

But when a medicine or treatment worked, doctors didn't know *why* it worked. The underlying theories that explain infections, and the inoculations and antibiotics that these theories produced, had to await the widespread use of the compound optical microscope (which was invented at the beginning of the seventeenth century but didn't become ubiquitous until the late nineteenth century). The microscope led to the discovery of cells and bacteria and allowed scientists to actually see how they worked.

In the late nineteenth and early twentieth centuries, scientists became international heroes as they eliminated, one after another, the major diseases that had been the scourge of humankind (e.g., smallpox, typhoid). Emboldened by this success, Western medical science began arrogantly rejecting age-old treatments and cures that could not be scientifically explained by the then-current level of technology.

The basic unit in biology, the cell, is about 20 micrometers in diameter—it takes about 10,000 human cells to cover the head of a pin. For physical

---

[21]The story of Edward Jenner's discovery of the cowpox vaccine to prevent smallpox is well-known. But it is not well-known that the actual process of inoculation itself (deliberately infecting someone with a disease to prevent that same disease from occurring) was developed in the East hundreds of years earlier and widely known in Jenner's time.

reasons, an optical microscope cannot resolve two points that are closer together than approximately one-half of the wavelength of the illuminating light—and an individual bacterial cell, for example, is approximately one-tenth the wavelength of visible light.[22]

Today we know that the critical biochemical functions performed by vitamins, minerals and nutritional supplements take place on a molecular versus a cellular level. And since each cell is composed of trillions of molecules, these functions cannot even be detected with an optical microscope.

Until the relatively recent invention of the electron microscope, which is still far from becoming as widespread as the optical microscope was in the 1800s, scientists were unable to study the molecular structure of cells and how they function. This led most western medical school training to virtually ignore the importance of nutrition and the effect of vitamins, minerals and natural supplements.

The eminent biologist Michael Behe talks about how the search for reliable knowledge is a long, difficult process that never reaches an end. For most of human history, scientists believed that all matter was made of only what they could see, namely the four "elements" of earth, air, fire and water. Biologists similarly believed that all living bodies were regulated by the four "humors"—blood, yellow bile, black bile and phlegm—and that all disease arose from an excess of one of these humors. Throughout history advancing technology expanded their vision, but often caused great upheaval in the scientific community. Behe points out that "during periods of upheaval, however, when apparently solid verities are

---

[22]Behe, Michael J., *Darwin's Black Box: The Biochemical Challenge to Evolution,* The Free Press, 1996, page 10.

questioned, it can seem as if nothing in the world makes sense."[23]

Professor Behe was referring to where we are in our current understanding of DNA research and human development. After immersing myself in the latest biological research on food and nutrition, I believe that his description of where we are in DNA research also holds true for human nutrition.

In the first appendix to this book I have summarized how food, vitamins and minerals function. While I have attempted to present the most current information available, our knowledge in this area is advancing so fast that much of it may already be superseded by a better theory by the time you read this book.

When it comes to new vitamins, minerals and natural supplements, the best advice I can offer you is to stay abreast of observations—clinical long-term studies of large groups—and especially note what works for you, your family and your associates. Do not pay attention to the "scientific theory of the day"—until its results have been proven in actual experience over time with large groups of people. And always remember that every vitamin, mineral, natural treatment and supplement is by definition "natural"—meaning that it is part of our food supply that developed along with our bodies over the millennia. In general, wherever possible, *you should make your medicine your food and your food your medicine.*

---

[23]Ibid., p 7.

*　　　　　*　　　　　*

Moses Maimonides, a twelfth-century rabbi and physician in Moorish Spain, is esteemed by Jews, Christians and Muslims alike as one of the greatest theologians of all time. Maimonides attempted to reconcile Greek philosophy with the Old and New Testaments. He concluded that our obligation to be healthy was a religious obligation, a first order of priority we must undertake before we begin to know our Creator.

In our time, some religious institutions have begun to encourage their congregants to control their diet. One program, the Weigh Down Diet, is based on the philosophy that overeating and gluttony are sins. Despite some controversy surrounding its founder, there are nearly 30,000 Weigh Down workshops, mostly in U.S. churches, making a real difference in the lives of millions of participants.[24]

The Weigh Down Diet and other programs stress the negative or sinful aspects of overeating. Despite the success of these programs, I believe the answer for the majority of Americans will lie in a more positive approach.

I was raised in a Jewish family that observed religious dietary laws, where I was not allowed to eat unkosher foods such as lobster, shrimp or pork. You can imagine how quickly I abandoned the kosher rules of my family upon turning 17 and going off to college. It wasn't until years after college, when I started spending time with deeply religious relatives in Israel, that I came to understand what I had missed growing up. To some observant Jews, the requirement to eat only the foods prescribed by

---

[24]Mead, Rebecca, "Slim for Him: God Is Watching What You're Eating," *The New Yorker,* January 15, 2001.

biblical law is not seen as deprivation, but as one of God's greatest gifts. They thank God for this knowledge in prayers before and after every meal. Eating kosher food is one of life's greatest *mitzvahs* (i.e., good deeds).

I believe that my parents were correct in their approach but misguided in its implementation, as they too had become exploited by the economic interests of the kosher food industry—an industry concerned more with labels and paid-for rabbinical blessings than in remaining true to God's original intention, as expressed through the laws of maintaining a kosher diet.

It is time to take a second look at the wisdom of the Greeks without the fear of our ancestors that such a look will lead us to stray from our monotheistic God. To the Greeks, physical strength, health and beauty were just as central to a man's *arete,* or "excellence," as his creative talents, intellect, industriousness or moral character. Indeed, outward beauty was believed to reflect the beauty within.

As noted earlier, for obvious reason, the people today most dedicated to *arete,* in its ancient sense, are the "professionally beautiful," those people who depend on maintaining their health and appearance to be successful. Movie stars, talk show hosts and other entertainment professionals in particular inhabit a secret world in which the physical fundamentals of life—food, exercise, vitamins, nutritional supplements, medical care and aging—are seen from a radically different perspective than that of most human beings. Along with other societal role models and many leading business executives, these wellness-oriented people have begun to reflect, in their daily lives, the revolution now occurring in the health and nutrition fields. Each act of apparent pain or denial, from strenuous sessions with their personal trainers to navigating through the menus at exclusive restaurants, is a positive, almost-religious experience. They focus on how they will feel hours later *because* of each laborious exercise, or on how much stronger they will feel that evening because of what they are not eating over lunch or dinner. This makes what seems painful to others become, to them, a euphoric experience with its own immediate rewards.

Some people imagine that the healthy life is one of deprivation, of constantly saying "no" to things we enjoy. But the wellness-oriented have learned to cherish and be grateful for the knowledge of how to take care of themselves. They value their healthy diets much as the Orthodox Jew or Muslim values his or her dietary laws, which have been passed down over the centuries. Through the small and reasonable disciplines of daily eating, a wellness-oriented individual and an orthodox Jew or Muslim both experience a sense of distinction, specialness and closeness to God.

I stopped eating meat about seven years ago for spiritual (versus dietary) reasons. I remember how those with whom I was having a meal would sometimes tell me how sorry they felt for me because of the "good" things I was denying myself. I didn't argue with them back then because I didn't want to impose my spiritual beliefs on others. Looking back, now that I also know the enormous health benefits that also come from a low- or no-meat diet, I regret having missed those opportunities to share my new-found gift of knowledge.

Back then, I thought I was "healthy" at age 40—I looked trim, fit, and had never been sick except for the occasional common cold once or twice a year. Now, after seven years of purifying my body and strengthening my immune system, I feel younger at age 47 than I ever did at age 20, let alone 40. Thanks to the addition of a regular program of exercise and diet supplementation, my stamina, mind and senses have sharpened beyond belief.

My father often told me the Socratic principle that the beginning of true knowledge is when you start to understand how little you know. If there is anything I learned most over the past seven years, it is that we have yet to approach the limits of how strong and healthy we can feel.

Too many people wait until their health is severely impaired before they take action. Or they think, like I did before age 40, that they are already fit and healthy—so why should they spend time trying to fix something that is not broken.

Improving your health is like climbing mountains—each peak you climb becomes the base from which you ascend to another higher range of mountains, the peaks of which were previously regarded as unreachable.

To get some idea of what is possible, stop and think of your relationship with someone you love— say, a parent, a spouse or a child. What would have been your response five years ago if I asked you then, on a scale of one to ten, how much you loved them? How would you have described your relationship back then?

Now think of how much more you love them today. If I could play a videotape today of your earlier response, would you be embarrassed when you compared it to the depth of your feelings for them today?

This is what awaits you as you embark on the path to improve your health—regardless of where you are starting out.

Chapter 3

The Next Trillion

There is no riches above a sound body.
The Apocrypha, Ecclesiasticus 30:16

I had two objectives in mind when I began researching and writing this book: (1) exposing the nefarious practices of the food and medical industries; and (2) teaching people the correct choices to make in order to be healthy and obtain good medical care.

Explaining new business opportunities for people to make money was not one of my objectives. Yet, after immersing myself in the food and medical research behind this book, I now see an emerging industry in which the greatest fortunes of the next century will be created—fortunes that will eclipse even those of the Internet billionaires of the late 1990s.

Approximately one-seventh of the U.S. economy today, about $1.4 trillion, is devoted to the healthcare business. The name "healthcare" is a misnomer; this one-seventh of the economy is really devoted to the "sickness" business—defined in the dictionary as "ill health, illness, a disordered, weakened, or unsound condition, or a specific disease."[25]

The sickness business is *reactive;* despite its enormous size, people only become customers when they are stricken by and react to a specific condition or ailment. No one really wants to be a customer.

---

[25]Merriam-Webster Collegiate Dictionary, ©1996 Zane Publishing, Inc. and Merriam-Webster, Inc.

By the year 2010, an additional $1 trillion of the U.S. economy, will be devoted to the yet-unnamed "wellness" business—defined in the dictionary as "the quality or state of being in good health *especially as an actively sought goal* (emphasis added)."[26]

The wellness business is *proactive*—people *voluntarily* become customers; partly to feel healthier and partly to avoid becoming customers of the sickness business. Everyone wants to be a customer.

From this point forward we will utilize the following definitions:

Sickness industry: Products and services provided *reactively* to people with an existing disease, ranging from a common cold to existing cancerous tumors. These products and services either seek to treat the symptoms of a disease or eliminate the disease.

Wellness industry: Products and services provided *proactively* to "healthy people" (those without an existing disease) to either make them feel even healthier, look better, slow down the effects of aging, or to prevent diseases from developing in the first place.

In promulgating these definitions, the line between the two industries sometimes must be drawn separately for each category of products and services.

For example, when it comes to surgery, a biological norm must be established. Cosmetic surgery solely to improve a person's appearance above a "normal" state would be considered part of wellness, whereas cosmetic surgery to repair a birth defect like a cleft lip would be considered part of

---

[26]Ibid.

sickness.

Lasik eye surgery to treat myopia would be considered part of wellness (i.e., cures the dysfunction), whereas supplying basic eyeglasses for myopia might be considered part of sickness (i.e., treating the symptom).

Some people join a fitness or health club to maintain or increase their overall strength. This would be considered part of wellness. People joining a fitness or health club primarily to lose weight could be considered part of sickness but we will define it as wellness. In fact, we will define the rapidly growing $50 billion U.S. weight loss business as part of wellness, although it could be argued that this money is spent by consumers in reaction to obesity, which is a disease. In the future, we would hope that the technology of the wellness industry will eliminate the need for the weight loss business, just as medical technology in the last century virtually eliminated major diseases from polio to typhoid.

Today, the nascent wellness industry encompasses some of the following businesses:

Vitamins
Nutritional supplements
Cosmetic plastic surgery
Voluntary eye surgery (Lasik, radial
    keratotomy)
Cosmetic dermatology
Genetic engineering (sex selection, fertility
    enhancement)
Cosmetic and reconstructive dentistry (caps,
    implants)
Fitness clubs (including trainers)
Fitness and athletic equipment
Voluntary pharmacy: Viagra (for impotence),
    Rogaine (for hair growth)
Health food products

Health food restaurants
Weight loss products

Although most of these businesses did not exist at
an economically significant level just one or two
decades ago, they already total approximately $200
billion in annual sales, about half the amount spent
on U.S. automobiles.[27]

Yet this amount represents just the tip of the
iceberg for the wellness industry in the next decade.

One major reason for this enormous growth
projection is demographics.

The birth rate of American citizens dramatically
increased after World War II. Between 1946 and 1964
approximately 78 million children were born in the
United States. In contrast, in the same period of time
before 1946, only 50 million births were recorded.
But in the same period of time after 1964, despite a
much larger population base, only 66 million births
were recorded.

This great bulge in the U.S. population is
generally referred to as the "baby boom" or the baby
boom generation. We define it as a "boom" because
birth rates rapidly declined after 1964; had this not
occurred the postwar birth rate increase would have
simply represented a long-term trend rather than an
event creating a distinct population group.

The significance of this fact cannot be overstated.

In any society, there seems to be a limit to the
number of topics that can occupy public concern at

---

[27]There is so much overlap between the different categories that
I have deliberately not listed each one with an exact amount of
current sales. For example, the vitamin industry claims current
sales of $70 billion—although a close examination of this number
yields the fact that it includes vitamins and supplements added
to ordinary foods. Similarly, the $12 billion in fitness club
revenues does not isolate amounts paid to the clubs themselves
for the use of their trainers.

a specific period in time. With a normally expanding population, these topics are typically dominated by the concerns and tastes of the younger members of the society, since there are simply more (and more) of them. However, the bulge in the U.S. population of those born between 1946 and 1964 has caused our topics of concern to be dominated by this group rather than those concerns of the *next* generation.

This phenomenon initially manifested itself in the late 1960s and early 1970s when certain "oldies" radio stations became more popular than contemporary ones—as the first baby boomers entering adulthood continued to listen to the music of their youth. Then, beginning in the 1970s we saw an increasing return of the "boomers" to the fashions of their youth in clothing, automobiles, housing, furniture, industrial design and commercial architecture. A new word was coined to define this phenomenon, "retro," which entered our vernacular (and our dictionary) in 1974.[28]

And now, as the baby boom generation (currently ages 35–54) is entering its most economically productive years, this phenomenon of catering to their concerns will accelerate even more. Their economic dominance will continue until sometime after 2010, when the first boomers turn 65 and their economic power and social influence begins to wane.

But the economic impact of this group on wellness is even stronger than its numbers suggest—because this group is behaving differently than any prior generation. Boomers are refusing to passively accept the aging process. A recent book explains it best from a marketing perspective:

---

[28]Retro—"relating to, reviving, or being the styles or esp. the fashions of the past: fashionably nostalgic or old-fashioned <a retro look>." ©1996 Zane Publishing, Inc. and Merriam-Webster, Inc.

"One of the most important truths about boomers is that they are still the youth market. In their teens and twenties...boomers created the youth market. As they enter their forties and fifties...boomers are proving the youth market to be a state of mind rather than a stage of life. Most boomers still live in that state, refusing to adopt the attitudes and lifestyles of their parents. . . . Businesses savvy enough to determine what boomers want will catch a wave of consumer demand that will be the ride of a lifetime."[29]

Boomers are already responsible for the largest stock market rise in history, the housing boom, the rise of international airlines, the personal computer, the Internet, the sport utility vehicle—in short, boomers are responsible for roughly $5 trillion today of our $10 trillion national economy. And these boomers are about to add an additional $1 trillion to our economy as they seek to preserve what they hold dearest: their youth.

In just the next ten years, U.S. boomers will increase their spending on existing wellness-based services from approximately $200 billion today to $1 trillion or more. This growth will come partly from the demographic expansion of the market as boomers move from ages 35–55 to ages 45–65, and partly from sales growth due to improvements in the efficacy of wellness-based products and services. Hundreds if not thousands of better wellness-based products and services are coming out of the laboratory the next ten years. This list includes improved types of vitamins and minerals, new supplements like echinacea that ward off colds and diseases, and natural hormone and soy-based

---

[29]Foreword, *The Baby Boom: Americans Aged 35 to 54,* 2nd ed. by Cheryl Russell. 1999, 2000 New Strategist Publications, Inc.

antiaging creams that truly retard wrinkles and impart youthful vitality to the cells they touch.

And this fivefold increase is just the beginning.

Just as boomers now set the pace for the desires of the next generation, from retro tastes in music to housing and independent lifestyles, boomers will set the pace for the wellness industry for generations to come. By 2010, Generation X, those born between 1965 and 1979, will be entering middle age. This and subsequent generations will take the boomer-established proactive approach to wellness and aging as standard medical procedure.

And, as we shall see in the next chapter, just as with the personal computer industry in the last two decades, each single sale of an efficacious wellness product or service will create its own continuing and increasing demand on the part of each individual for more wellness products and services. But these items, which will establish the stability of the wellness industry by 2010 and beyond, pale in comparison to genetically-based wellness products and services that will eventually be coming out of the laboratory.

*   *   *

"How sad it is!" murmured Dorian Gray with his eyes still fixed upon his own portrait. "How sad it is! I shall grow old, and horrible, and dreadful. But this picture will remain always young. It will never be older than this particular day of June. . . . If it were only the other way! If it were I who was to be always young, and the picture that was to grow old! For that—for that—I would give everything! Yes, there is nothing in the whole world I would not give! I would give my soul for that!"

The Picture of Dorian Gray, Oscar Wilde (1891)

The individual cells in our body are constantly dying and replacing themselves.[30] On a cellular level, the biochemical objective of most wellness activity is to ensure that these individual cells receive the raw materials—proteins, vitamins and minerals—necessary to remanufacture themselves at the optimal level.

But, at some point in a person's life, "something" tells each cell in each bodily organ to stop reproducing itself. This causes normal aging, illness, and eventually death. Or sometimes, even when a cell or organ does not suffer from a biochemical deficiency, "something" tells abnormal cells in an organ to uncontrollably multiply until they impair the function of that organ (e.g., cancer). Today we know that this "something" is one of the many and complex instructions in the genetic code for life, commonly referred to as DNA, or deoxyribonucleic acid. DNA is an organic compound found in all cells that contains the genetic code for inherited characteristics and replication.

Our genetic code is a human "text" with over three billion different letters—written entirely in four characters (A, T, C and G) with no spaces or punctuation. While the actual substance we now call DNA was discovered in 1869, its role in inheritance was only demonstrated in the latter half of the twentieth century, and the complete mapping of the human genome was not completed until the beginning of this century.[31]

---

[30]Our bodies manufacture 200 billion red blood cells each day, replacing all the blood in our body every 120 days. Skin is completely replaced every 1 to 3 months. It takes 90 days for old bone to be broken down and replaced by new bone.

[31]Watson and Crick received the Nobel Prize for discovering DNA in 1953, and Dr. J. Craig Venter of the Celera Corporation announced that they had completed mapping the human genome on April 6, 2000.

Our demand for wellness-based products and services is primarily driven by one function of the genetic code which causes aging—from the wrinkles that appear in our skin to the ultimate breakdown of our bodily organs. Over the long term, the understanding and eventual manipulation of this genetic code holds the greatest promise for the wellness industry.

By examining a person's DNA, which can be taken from the mouth with just a small swab or scraping device, it is already possible to predict the probability that a person will develop certain diseases. And soon, based on the recently completed mapping of the human genome, it should be possible to predict every forthcoming disease or condition not caused by external (i.e., diet and exercise) factors. Scientists expect this type of genetic testing to become widespread by 2010.[32] In just the next few years, by using this information to predict the probability to develop a certain condition, a wellness distributor could suggest a vitamin- or supplement-based therapy.

For example, a person with a genetic propensity to develop osteoporosis would be directed to take calcium supplements, or a person with a genetic propensity for developing prostate problems would be an early candidate to take saw palmetto.

Eventually, as technology progresses, vitamins and supplements used in this manner may be supplanted by genetic intervention—the actual modification or repair of the problematic gene containing the propensity to develop the disease. (Scientists do not expect this type of intervention to become effective in treating the full spectrum of

---

[32]Robert Bazell, "Scientists Map Human Chromosome," 1 December 1999, *NBC Nightly News.*

genetically   determined   diseases   for   several
decades.[33])

---

[33]Ibid.

Chapter 4
Demand

The baby-boomer demand for wellness products and services is being driven by two major factors.

First, new alternative medical products are becoming available on a widespread basis. When consumers see the efficacy of just one of these products, they often become voracious customers with an unlimited appetite for more wellness products and services.

And second, as shown in Chapters Six and Seven, the current sickness-based health insurance system will eventually be replaced for many Americans by a new wellness-based system that will gladly pay for weight reduction, nutritional advice, vitamins, minerals, smoking cessation and hundreds of other wellness-related or preventative treatments.

But before we examine these powerful developments, which will take the U.S. wellness industry to $1 trillion and beyond by 2010, it is important to understand the nature of demand in our modern economy, and what is fueling the economic expansion of both the past and the current decades.

*　　　　　*　　　　　*

Many Americans barely had enough to eat during the Great Depression of the 1930s. But even back then, the economist John Maynard Keynes could foresee that advancing U.S. technology would be able to supply the American people with everything they could want.

Lord Keynes made this optimistic prediction to U.S. president Franklin D. Roosevelt—that one day soon most American families would have a telephone, an automobile, and a four-bedroom, one-bathroom house with indoor plumbing. But, the economist warned the president, once people had fulfilled this American dream, they would lose their incentive to work. These productive Americans would stop spending their increasing income and start saving it, bringing the economy to a halt—a victim, as it were, of its own success.

Therefore, Keynes argued, the government should adopt policies, like progressive income taxation, to keep the most productive people in society working harder and from hoarding more and more of their earnings as their income increased.

This was radical thinking back then. When the (flat rate) federal personal income tax was first established in 1913, some policymakers thought it unfair that a person earning $100,000 a year would pay ten times the amount of federal taxes paid by a person earning $10,000 a year—yet both had equally only one vote. But only two decades later in 1936 Keynes was advocating raising federal income tax rates on a progressive scale so that the more a person was earning, the higher (and higher) his or her percentage income tax rate would be.

Thanks to Keynes and the U.S. policymakers who followed his advice, individual federal income tax rates rose throughout the twentieth century, reaching peak marginal rates of 92–94 percent by 1964 before stabilizing at 70 percent until the 1980s.[34]

---

[34]Most people think that Keynes had a greater impact during his time than he actually did. Many of the government programs of the 1930s and 1940s that are attributed to Keynes' recommendations were actually part of a larger phenomenon— active government involvement in the economy—that merely used Keynes' *General Theory* after the fact to justify their continued existence. The actual New Deal programs of the 1930s preceded the *General Theory* by several years.

As Chapter Six will show in detail, to avoid these insidious rates of taxation, corporations lobbied Congress for the right to pay certain employees with nontaxable perks such as company-provided medical care for them and their immediate families. This, more than any other single economic factor, has led to the problems we have in the United States today with escalating medical costs.

It has been said that one can learn more from studying the mistakes of our greatest minds rather than studying where they were correct. Today we know that while Keynes' theory, increasing affluence breeds complacency and oversaving, seemed logical when he wrote it, it is incorrect. The very opposite of what Keynes predicted has come to pass.

Looking back at the time when Keynes developed his landmark theory of oversaving, it is easy to see where he went wrong. During the 1930s, an insufficiency of consumer demand was the root cause of the continued depression—nothing the government could do seemed to be able to get consumers spending again. Keynes was convinced that doom was inevitable again unless the government established higher income tax rates on increasing personal income, and then injected this money back into the economy through increased government spending.

But over the last century, and especially the last two decades, upscale consumer demand has proven itself insatiable. The more we earn, the more we spend; the more we spend, the more we get; the more we get, the more we want; and the more we want, the harder we seem to be willing to work to earn more money to get it. If any segment of our society has lost the incentive to work, it is the very poor whom we seem unable to help get over the hurdle of purchasing their *first* cars or their *first* houses—purchases that lead to the never-ending cycle of unlimited consumer demand.

In the world we live in today, where advancing technology has been able to meet the basic primary needs for most Americans, advancing technology is constantly creating its own demand—offering new products and services that before too long become considered basic primary needs by the majority of the population.

Before the invention of the first electric washing machine around World War I, few Americans cared how many times they wore a shirt before they washed it, and clothing was constructed to require a minimum number of washings—shirts, for example, came with detachable collars and cuffs, the parts that got dirty most quickly.[35] Once the washing machine became available on a widespread basis every American had to wear a clean shirt every day—and detachable collars and cuffs went the way of the horse and buggy.

When Henry Ford first invented a mass-produced automobile that was affordable by the common man, people scoffed at the thought of who would buy it—there were few paved roads available to go anywhere, no gasoline stations, and most people lived within walking distance of where they worked. Then, thanks to the automobile, most people actually moved to a place—suburbia—where they needed it, gasoline stations proliferated, and soon the car became a necessity just to get to work or shop for daily necessities.

Back when the telephone first became available to businesses, most businessmen communicated through hand-delivered written messages that they

---

[35]The first electrically powered washing machine was invented in 1910 by Alva J. Fisher, but the product did not become widely available until the invention of an electrically powered agitator-type washer by Howard Snyder in 1922.

originated by dictating to their secretaries. Many of them were convinced that using the telephone was a waste of time. After all, who wanted to dictate a message to a secretary, have it transcribed, then read by the secretary over the telephone to the recipient's secretary, and then transcribed by the recipient's secretary into a written message for the recipient. Of course, before long the telephone changed the way in which businesspeople communicated; they spoke directly to one another rather than through notes transcribed by their secretaries. Thus the telephone became an absolute necessity for every business. (This story contains an important lesson for us today, as most people still use computers and other new inventions to merely modify existing obsolete ways of doing things—rather than reengineer the work itself to fit the ability of newly available tools.)

Today almost 95 percent of the things we spend our money on—which most of us think of as *necessities*—were not even around when many of us were born. Fax machines, television sets, airline travel, Disneyland vacations, high-fashion clothing, stereos, DVDs, air conditioners, personal computers, day care, movies, fast-food restaurants, dry cleaning, Internet access—the list goes on and on. Even the so-called traditional necessities like food, clothing and housing are no longer necessities in the sense that we consume quantities of them far in excess of our basic needs. In 1935 the average American lived in 136 square feet of living space versus over 750 square feet today.

The reason that consumer demand is so unlimited has to do with the nature of the two types of demand in our technological society—*quantity demand* and *quality demand.*

As illogical as it may seem at first, *quantity demand* is the consumer's desire for more of what he or she already has just purchased: another television set, a second car, a bigger house, an extra suit of clothing—even if he or she has never purchased such an item before.

Consider a young person first entering the work force upon graduation. Now, possibly for the first time in his or her life, they need business attire to wear to work. He or she proudly goes out to the store and purchases a first suit. But on the first day of work it becomes clear what else is needed: more suits, so they don't have to wear the same thing every day, not to mention ties, scarves, shirts and shoes to match.

Or think of a young couple buying their first automobile. The automobile changes everything for them: where they work, how they travel, where they dine, etc. But they soon realize their new need for something they hadn't even dreamed of before: a second car, so they can each independently get to work and shop. Similarly, a family might purchase a second television set for their bedroom, only to quickly discover the need now for a third set in the room of their child or in their kitchen.

A first house may seem to be the ultimate purchase for many young people starting out, yet it's actually just the beginning, as the home acquisition ignites never-ending demand for furniture, kitchen appliances, entertainment equipment and so on. New home construction is the most important indicator in forecasting most types of retail sales.

Savvy retailers of every product or service know that a purchase by a satisfied customer is just the beginning, rather than the ending, of their relationship. A men's clothing store might sell 100 "first" suits a year to young people just entering the work force, but 2,000 suits a year to consumers who already own one or more. The most important marketing information to an automobile dealer is what type of car the potential consumer already owns. And for every first-time home buyer in the United States each year there are at least five homes sold to existing homeowners moving on to (typically) larger ones.[36]

But at some point, a classical economist might argue, demand must be sated. After all, how many new suits, cars, homes and televisions can a consumer own?

The incorrect answer to this seemingly obvious question is where many once-successful merchants have met their match.

When *quantity demand* is satiated—as it is these days among a majority of Americans—*quality demand* kicks in. When you have all the food, clothing and TVs you need—as most Americans do today—you start wanting better food, better clothing and better TVs.

Quantity demand reflects the consumer's demand for a larger supply of an existing product; **quality demand** reflects the appetite for a different or improved kind of product.

In the case of TV sets, *quality demand* reflects a consumer's more sophisticated yearning for a better TV (e.g., a big-screen color receiver with remote-control capability and six-channel sound) as well as for related but otherwise entirely new products (e.g., a TIVO satellite receiver or a DVD player).

A typical middle-class couple would probably have little if any interest in buying a third sedan to add to the two they already own. But they might jump at the chance to get rid of one of the sedans and upgrade to a new sport utility vehicle (SUV). A young executive whose closet was filled with eight $200 suits would probably have little interest in

---

[36]U.S. Department of Commerce, Bureau of the Census, *Statistical Abstract of the United States: 1991* (Washington: Government Printing Office, 1991), 1272, 1275.

purchasing a ninth one. But he or she might jump at the chance to purchase a new $400 designer suit.

Moreover, this flip in the nature of demand is not one-way. For as the consumer begins to satisfy his or her desire for higher quality, *quantity demand* once again begins to work its magic. Now the couple wants two SUVs so they don't argue over who has to drive the sedan. Now the young executive wants seven $400 designer suits because he or she no longer feels "right" wearing the older $200 ones. Theoretically, of course, the demand for more and better goods will be satiated when the consumer finally owns a sufficiently large number of the best cars or best suits on the market. But as long as technology continues to advance, there never will be a best car or a best suit—at least not for very long. Each year a better one will be developed, and the process will start all over again.

Ironically, when it comes to understanding Western consumers, no one seems to understand us better than the Japanese.

In the 1960s, the Japanese overwhelmed many of the world's markets with inexpensive products—in effect, satiating *quantity demand.* But in the early 1970s they turned their attention to increasing the quality of their goods, riding the shift from *quantity demand* to *quality demand* (leaving the now unprofitable market for cheaper goods to their imitators). In less than twenty years, they went from being known as the lowest-cost producer of almost everything consumers could want to being known as the highest-quality (and usually the highest-priced) producer of almost everything.

In the 1990s the Japanese even dumped many of their traditional brand names like Datsun and Toyota in favor of new ones like Nissan and Lexus. And they left General Motors in the dust wondering why GM's satisfied Chevrolet customers weren't buying any more Chevrolets.

The consumer's continual desire for higher quality items is so incorporated into our marketplace that it is often transparent. Each year as advancing technology lowers the cost of products and services, smart producers and providers recognize that they want to keep existing customer relationships. In order to do so, they automatically improve the quality of their products rather than lower the price.

Suppose you spent $600 on a 27-inch color television in 1990 and went out in 2000 to buy its replacement at the same store. You would have found that virtually the same television now costs only $300 (actually $229 in 1990 dollars after adjusting for inflation). But rather than purchase the same television you would have probably elected to spend $600 again ($458 in 1990 dollars) to purchase a 35-inch model—or perhaps elected to spend $1,500 ($1,144 in 1990 dollars) on a super-deluxe high-definition model with six-channel sound and picture-in-picture channel displays. Moreover, you might not even have found the $300 model at your local store, as your merchant, aware that their satisfied customers wanted increasing quality rather than lower prices, no longer carried the (now) lower-end market models.

Or suppose in 1995 you entered medical school hoping to purchase a new $45,000 convertible automobile upon completing your residency in 2001. When you went to the dealer in 2001 you would have found that the car with all the features you wanted back then now cost only $25,000. But rather than purchase this car and pocket the $20,000 savings, you would most likely have traded up to a now-$45,000 car that had twice the features of the car you wanted back in 1995.

This consumer-driven phenomenon of choosing increasing quality over lower price is so prevalent today that most people don't realize how much the material quality of their lives has steadily increased—thanks to the improved quality, safety and lower prices of their products. Whether you are talking about TVs or toys, automobiles or air conditioners, blue jeans or bedding, digital cameras or convertible sofas, refrigerators or recorded music, people today invariably enjoy better quality goods at a lower real cost than they did at any other time in history.

It wasn't too long ago that when a person was late the most common reasons were either a flat tire or a flooded carburetor—problems that advancing technology (radial tires and electronic fuel injection) have almost completely eliminated from our daily concerns. Note also that these same technologies have quadrupled the mileage we get from each tire and doubled fuel economy—effectively quadrupling and doubling the supposedly "scarce" supply of resources used to manufacture tires and gasoline.

Paradoxically, lower prices and increased quality products are sometimes reported in our media as a decrease rather than an increase in our material wealth. This is because our most common economic indicators, such as Gross Domestic Product (GDP) or retail sales, are not indexed for either increasing quality or for price deflation caused by the ability of technology to lower prices. For example, when the medical student in our example purchased his $45,000 car, he experienced a $20,000 unreported increase in his material lifestyle—or if he had purchased his $45,000 original dream car for $25,000, it would have shown up as a $20,000 decrease in GDP or retail sales.

Similarly, when the average cost of a new home is reported by the U.S. government, this figure is not indexed for the fact that it is more than twice the size of the average new home in the 1960s, or that it contains features and appliances that alone make it worth twice as much to the consumer. Most of us were raised in a typical middle-class house of 1960—say about 900 square feet without a dishwasher or air-conditioning—which today could be considered a fairly primitive standard of living compared to a new home in 2001, which averages about 2,300 square feet and contains a host of modern appliances and conveniences.

* * *

Back in the 1930s, Keynes was brilliant in being able to foresee the end of scarcity due to the advance of technology. But Keynes was mistaken in his inability to see that this same advancing technology would lead to a never-ending demand for more of the same products and services. Or was he?

Consumers typically spend increasing disposable income on luxury goods and leisure activities—often on new products and services that didn't exist when they were born. However, a close examination of some of these new products and services yields a paradox that could limit their growth in the future.

Almost all new luxury products, from Harley-Davidson motorcyles to computer games to garden tractors, have one major drawback: They take time to enjoy. This is one of the great paradoxes of modern life: Each year consumers seem to get more and more disposable income but less and less time to enjoy it. In contrast to the "idle rich" and "working poor" stereotypes of the past, disposable income today is inversely proportional to leisure time at almost every class level. When you asked someone yesterday why they hadn't bought some particular new item, a typical response might have been that they couldn't afford it. Today, a more typical response might be that they haven't had time to play with the new item they bought over a week or month ago.

Moreover, an increasing amount of the growth in consumer demand today is in the entertainment and services sector rather than in physical products. These time-consuming purchases, ranging from massages to luxury cruises to opera tickets, have their own built-in demand limitation—the 24-hour day and the 365-day year. Many consumers report that their main time constraint today comes from other leisure activities rather than from their work itself.

Thus, while Keynes was mistaken in not seeing that once consumers got what they wanted they would want more of what they wanted, Keynes could eventually be proven correct in his belief that there is some nonmonetary limit to consumer demand. Unless, of course, technology could come up with products and services desired by consumers that did not take time to enjoy.

Wellness products and services represent perhaps the only sector of consumer spending that does not take time to enjoy. Monies spent to make a person feel stronger, smile better, look younger, or feel healthier yield rewards that are enjoyed every moment of every day—on the job, at home and at every moment in between.

This may seem obvious when stated but is often not realized, since consumers only recently have had the option to purchase wellness products and services. Until now, *most people were told to accept their wellness deficiencies as part of the aging process, as if there was nothing they could do about them.*

One of the fastest growing sectors of the wellness industry today is the vitamin and nutritional supplement business. But until very recently, this business was almost entirely limited to treating sickness. Scurvy, or vitamin C deficiency, is one of the oldest known nutritional disorders, and its symptoms were written about in Crusader history. It was the major cause of disability and mortality among British sailors until Scottish physician James Lind noted that the Dutch had employed citrus fruits to eliminate scurvy. In 1795 the consumption of lime juice became mandatory on all British naval vessels—and people of British descent are still called "limeys" to this day.

Rickets, or vitamin D deficiency, was noted throughout history and caused skeletal deformities, especially in children. Beginning in the eighteenth century it was treated with cod-liver oil and sunlight.[37]

Beriberi, or vitamin B1 deficiency, is caused by the unnatural removal of this vitamin from processed rice and other grains. Beriberi literally means "extreme weakness" in Sinhalese and has been noted in Asian countries since polished white rice became a staple more than 1,000 years ago.[38] In all of these cases, scientists only recognized these nutritional deficiencies when they manifested themselves as terrible sickness.

Then, in the twentieth century it was discovered that there are 13 essential vitamins required to maintain good health that generally cannot be manufactured in the body.[39] And more recently, it has been discovered that these same vitamins are

---

[37]Today, this terrible disease has been almost completely eradicated through the addition of vitamin D to commonly consumed foods.

[38]The cause of beriberi was discovered by Casimir Funk in 1912. It has been eradicated through the addition of Vitamin B1, or thiamine, back into dehusked grains.

[39]Vitamins contain no energy directly but are required catalysts in order to produce the hundreds of chemical reactions required for sustaining life. Since they generally cannot be manufactured by the body they must be obtained elsewhere on a daily basis.

able to prevent disease from developing, make us feel even "better than well," and even slow the aging process itself.[40]

Today almost 50 percent of Americans take some sort of nutritional supplement, and industry sales for these products exceed $70 billion. Yet the vitamin and mineral industry has only scratched the surface of what is possible. For we are just beginning to understand the biochemistry that explains how vitamins, minerals and other supplements work.

As explained in Chapter Two, when it comes to understanding how our cells function on a molecular level, we are today where the sickness industry was prior to the nineteenth century—we know what works but we do not yet fully understand why something works. Yet medicine established itself as a major science long before the widespread use of the optical microscope was able to explain so many of its mysteries.

Similarly, we have already seen the wellness industry garner about $200 billion in U.S. annual sales even though science does not yet understand the molecular secrets behind much of its efficacy. And, even if we don't uncover these secrets in the near future, this $200 billion is just the beginning. Here's why.

Many potential customers have never even heard of wellness products and services, let alone tried them. Medical science has told people for too long to expect and accept declining health and energy levels as they age—partially because many doctors have only rudimentary training in nutrition and partially because the ultimate payor or the provider of medical

---

[40]Our bodies age or decay over time due to molecules called free radicals, which cause them to oxidate or "rust." Certain vitamins may be able to slow or retard oxidation.

services (employers) do not have financial incentives to pay for wellness.

Yet each of us knows someone who has recently had a wellness experience: a single mother who changed her diet and lost 35 pounds; a boy with a new vitamin regimen who now focuses twice as hard in school; a father using magnetic therapy who has eliminated chronic pain; a girl taking echinacea who no longer misses school because of colds; a former athlete using glucosamine who has returned to bicycling without knee problems; or a patient with an enlarged prostate who avoided painful surgery by taking saw palmetto. The list goes on and on.

Now think for a moment what else happened to this person's life after an initial wellness experience.

The single mother probably has a new schedule that includes regular athletic activity like jogging; the boy is trying out for sports since his academics are under control; the father wants to develop more energy to keep up with his children since pain no longer dominates his thoughts; the girl's parents want to know what supplements they should be giving their other children; the former athlete wants to improve his memory since he now believes in nutritional supplementation; and the former prostate patient has completely changed his diet and now wants to learn everything about alternative medical treatments.

In each of these cases, the initial purchase of a single wellness product or service ignited *quantity demand*—the demand for more of what they had just purchased—even though they didn't even know it had existed before they purchased it. And, when the wellness product or service had worked its magic, it ignited *quality demand*—the demand for different and/or better wellness products and services.

Each satisfied wellness customer is just beginning a lifetime of consumption of products and services that have the potential to improve every aspect of their life for every moment of their life. More than any other factor, this unlimited propensity to consume wellness products and services will take the wellness industry to $1 trillion and beyond by 2010.

Chapter 5

Distribution

It is difficult to predict today which manufacturing companies will succeed in the emerging $1 trillion wellness industry. It is even more difficult to predict who will succeed in wellness distribution, especially since some of the best wellness products are still in the laboratory. And even if I could tell you which companies today are best poised for success, much of the information would be quickly outdated—if only because the companies least poised for success would be busy retooling their products and their management. Fortunately, though, we can learn much about the wellness distribution opportunities of the future by examining recent changes in the distribution of other consumer products. Then we can apply this information to new opportunities as they come along.

In business and technology, whenever we study the past, we must do so with an important caveat: *Changes that used to take place in 50 years or more now take place in 5 years or less.*

In 1981, it took only seven years for the 70-year-old carburetor industry to be displaced by electronic fuel injection. In 1985, it took only 5 years for the 50-year-old phonograph record to be displaced by the compact disc. In 1995, it took only 3 years for the 30-year old fax machine to be largely displaced by e-mail. In studying the past, it is necessary to condense time when considering solutions applicable to the future—as changes that now take place in five years may soon take place in five months, or even less.

*   *   *

The most important economic concept underlying our modern economy is the biologically-based principle of unlimited wealth. Here's an exercise I use to teach this concept to children in grade school:

I have the members of the class pretend they are shipwrecked on a desert island with no provisions. In order to survive, they must organize a society and divide the work according to specific chores—like gathering food, building shelters and collecting firewood.

At first, the students want to rotate democratically various chores in their new island society. However, as we role-play out the various chores, they soon learn that it is much better for each person to specialize.

The person who goes out to find apples on Monday not only returns with apples, she knows exactly where to get the apples on Tuesday. By Wednesday, she not only knows where to find the apples, she has made tools like a sack or a wheelbarrow to carry them all back to the camp in one trip. By Thursday, she has made a tool to pick the ripe apples from the higher branches before they fall to the ground. By Friday, since she is now able to accomplish a former day's work in less than an hour, she starts learning how to make apple cider and apple preserves.

Eventually, all of the chores (obtaining food, shelter, fuel, etc.) are performed in a fraction of the time and by a fraction of the people originally required to complete them. This frees some members of the society to explore new pursuits—producing new products and tools and even providing entertainment.

As the society grows, so much quantity and variety of goods are produced that a new need arises—distributing all these goods and services. Before long some people are engaged full-time in distribution—which mostly entails educating everyone about what the others are doing and what is available. These distributors, or merchants, end up being the wealthiest members of the island society because they add the most value—especially when the island society encounters another island society and the merchants begin trading tools as well as produce.

In this lesson my students learn the two main principles underlying our modern economy. First, over time there is no limit to the amount individuals can produce of a single good or service by making use of the advancing technology that automatically results from specialization. Second, the total overall wealth of a society is limited only by the number of individuals available to trade with for their specialized tools and produce.[41]

The economic power of the United States is based, in part, on distribution laws that initially made it the world's largest open marketplace for goods and services. The original U.S. Constitution allowed each state to rule itself—have its own courts, its own militia and even make its own laws regarding slavery—with one very powerful exception: No state was allowed to make any law or rule that infringed upon the rights of its citizens to freely trade with the citizens of any other state.

Similarly, the economic power of the developed

---

[41]At this point I also ask the schoolchildren to vote on whether we should invite a passing ship of 50 destitute foreign schoolchildren to come live on our island and share our newly developed wealth. If the lesson has been successful, during the ensuing debate the students realize themselves that they, and the new immigrants, will both become even richer when the newcomers are welcomed with open arms into our island society.

nations today—Western Europe, North America, Japan and the other Asian tigers (Taiwan, South Korea, Singapore, etc.)—is also based on effectively free trade between their one billion or so citizens. The challenge today for the less developed nations is how to allow their five billion people to join the free traders, while fighting the political instability at home that often results from rapid economic change.

Throughout history, there have been fortunes made and fortunes lost in manufacturing or in controlling some particular commodity. But the only consistent success has come from distributing the ever-expanding production of the latest technology.

In the 1967 movie *The Graduate,* Dustin Hoffman was offered a confident, one-word solution to the quest for economic success: "Plastics." Back then, due to a short-term shortage of raw materials that peaked in the 1970s, economic success for many did lie in finding less expensive ways to make things.

Today, however, thanks to "plastics" and so many other better ways of making things, economic success for most people no longer lies in manufacturing. Today the greatest opportunities lie in the distribution sector of our economy.

Back in 1967 a manufactured product that sold for $300, for example, such as a camera or a fashionable dress, typically had a manufacturing cost of approximately $150 and a distribution cost of approximately $150. Distribution costs then accounted for approximately 50 percent of retail prices.

Today, the same product of similar quality typically retails for approximately $100 (although many people don't realize this because they have shifted to purchasing higher-quality products). This two-thirds price reduction for similar quality items has occurred primarily because technology has lowered production costs all the way from $150 to approximately $30 or less. Distribution costs have also fallen, from $150 to approximately $70, to where they now account for approximately 70 percent of the price for a typical $100 retail product.

TYPICAL RETAIL PRODUCT COST BREAKDOWN

	1967		2001	
	$	%	$	%
Manufacturing Costs	$150	50%	$ 30	30%
Distribution Costs	$150	50%	$ 70	70%
Total Retail Price	$300	100%	$100	100%

The reason that distribution costs have not fallen as much as manufacturing costs is that we have just begun to apply to distribution many of the innovative methods that we had already applied to manufacturing.[42]

Thus, in the 1960s it was possible to make a great deal of money by lowering the costs of production. Back then even a 10 or 20 percent reduction in manufacturing costs could lower your retail price by $15 or $30. Fortunes were made by those who found ways to lower manufacturing costs all the way from $150 to $30 or less, often by using "plastics" or relocating production facilities overseas.

Today, where manufacturing costs now represent about $30 of a typical $100 retail price, a 10 or 20

---

[42]Readers of my prior books may note that distribution costs were estimated in 1990 at 80 percent (versus 70 percent today). Distribution costs as a percentage of retail sales fell throughout the 1990s due to the advent of the Internet (or real-time information sharing) as we'll examine more in a moment, but the same advent of the Internet lowered manufacturing costs at an even greater pace.

percent reduction in manufacturing costs might only represent a $3 to $6 retail price reduction on a $100 item.

But today, where distribution costs now represent about $70 of a typical $100 retail price, a 10 or 20 percent reduction in distribution costs might represent a $7 to $14 retail price reduction on a $100 item. A 50 percent or greater reduction in distribution costs—sometimes feasible by just eliminating one link in the distribution chain between the factory and the consumer—might represent a $35 or even greater retail price reduction on a $100 item.

Due primarily to the increased role of distribution costs, many of the production facilities that moved overseas in previous years have now moved back to the United States. The majority of the "foreign" cars sold in the United States are now made in the United States. The largest auto plant in the world is the Honda Accord plant in Marysville, Ohio—which even exports much of its production to Japan—and the hottest new line of Mercedes SUVs are made in Alabama.

Increasing relative distribution costs are why, in the past three decades, the majority of the great personal fortunes have been made by people who found better ways of distributing things rather than better ways of making things. For example, by 1992 the richest man in the world was a person who had only started his company at age 44 in the 1960s and never "made" anything in his life: the late Sam Walton, founder of Wal-Mart. Or the person who became a billionaire in the 1970s by founding an entire airline for distributing products rather than people: Fred Smith of Federal Express. Or the person who became a billionaire in the 1980s by discovering better ways of distributing other companies' hardware and software: Ross Perot of EDS.

And more recently, the megafortunes of Internet billionaires like Jeff Bezos of Amazon.com, who was chosen as *Time* magazine's Man of the Year in 1999, were made primarily by those who found ways to use a new tool (the Internet) to distribute things better.

But when we look closer, especially at the fortunes that have been made most recently, we see that the nature of the distribution opportunity has changed. Distribution is really two processes: First, distribution is educating consumers about products and services that will improve their lives. And second, distribution is physically distributing products and services to consumers.

Sam Walton, Fred Smith and most of the distribution billionaires of the twentieth century made their fortunes by finding better and cheaper ways to physically distribute products to consumers *that consumers already knew they wanted.*

However, Jeff Bezos and the distribution billionaires of the twenty-first century are making their distribution fortunes mostly by educating consumers about new products and services— typically products and services *that consumers didn't even know were available.*

This flip-flop in the nature of the distribution opportunity has occurred before.

Prior to the nineteenth century, the work of distribution (of finished goods) mostly entailed educating consumers about products and services that would improve their lives. The peddler and the Main Street merchant alike prided themselves on the knowledge of what they sold, and explaining their products to customers took up the bulk of their time.

In the nineteenth century, these peddlers and merchants evolved into the department stores that characterized most of twentieth-century distribution. From Marshall Field's in Chicago (1865) to Filene's in Boston (1881), utilizing technological advances like the centralization of credit, real estate and buying functions, department stores quickly replaced the peddlers and individual Main Street merchants from whom they themselves had sprung.

These department stores did a lot more than just use technology to lower the cost of selling merchandise. They prided themselves on the customer service of small retailers. This fueled the never-ending cycle of consumer demand that defied then-conventional economic logic. Instead of going to the department store to purchase something you wanted, you went to the department store to find out about something you didn't know existed but that you couldn't live without once you learned about it (like electric lamps, dishwashers, icemakers and self-cleaning ovens).

Looking back on those days before the advent of television and mass media, the department store best served the two distinct functions of distribution today. The department store first *educated* its customers about new products that would improve their lives. Then, once it had taught customers what was available and assisted them in choosing the right product for their needs, it *physically distributed* the product from the factory to the consumer.

From this point forward we will utilize the following definitions: *intellectual distribution* and *physical distribution.*

Intellectual distribution is the process of educating customers about products and services, typically items that they either don't know exist or don't know are now affordable.

Physical distribution is the process of helping customers physically obtain products and services that they already know they want.

Every retailer today, or for that matter virtually every business today, performs these two functions in serving their customers.

From 1950–2000 the traditional department stores declined partly because advancing technology, like universal credit cards and shopping malls, made most of their original innovations (like charge accounts) obsolete. But department stores declined mostly because they failed to keep their physical distribution service at the level of their intellectual distribution service.

As the consumer retail dollar shifted from traditional durables (e.g., major appliances, furniture) to more consumables (e.g., cleaners, paper towels, batteries), consumers desired to quickly obtain these items—items that they already knew they wanted—in as short a time as possible and on a regular basis. The physical layout of the typical multistory department store was ill-suited to this task, and the department stores were slow to retool their layout. Many of us can remember running into a department store to buy a roll of film, only to have to wait while the same clerk who operated the cash register took 10 minutes to explain a new camera to a potential customer.

This led entrepreneurs like Sam Walton to open mass-merchandise stores dedicated almost entirely to physical versus intellectual distribution. These stores sold the customer exactly, and only, what they knew they wanted before they entered the store—in the shortest time possible and at the lowest possible price. The mass-merchandisers decimated the traditional department stores.[43]

---

[43]Not every department store owner was asleep at the switch. The century-old Dayton-Hudson Corporation (i.e., Marshall Field's, Mervyn's, Dayton-Hudson), successfully retooled its existing department stores toward more fashionable merchandise

The mass-merchandisers also benefited from the development of radio and television. Mass media allowed manufacturers of wide-appeal products to bypass the traditional department stores in communicating directly with their customers.

Today most manufacturers "handshake" with their customers through the mass media, and the surviving retailers for most products are the lowest cost, most efficient, physical distributors of merchandise—like Wal-Mart, K-Mart and Target Stores. Customer loyalty has shifted from individual retailers—like Sears, Macy's and J.W. Robinson's—to individual manufacturers—like Sony, Levi's and the brands of Procter & Gamble.

When this trend began 30 years ago a commonly heard shopping complaint was that the customer knew more than the clerks about what they were selling. Today most retail-store shoppers assume that *they* are more educated about their purchases than the people who sell them.

More recently, a new retailing trend has emerged, category-busting, which attempts to preserve the physical distribution benefits of the mass-merchandisers while adding some intellectual distribution components.

These category-busters, which include stores like Home Depot, PetsMart, CompUSA, Toys "R" Us and Babies "R" Us, are effectively mass-merchants for just one category of merchandise. These stores carry the largest array of merchandise in their category at the lowest prices, which makes consumers willing to travel greater distances to reach them, which allows

---

while simultaneously building Target Stores from scratch in 1962 into one of the world's largest mass-merchandisers. In fact, they were so successful that the Target division exceeded 78 percent of their $33 billion in sales in 1999, and the company changed its name to Target Corporation in 2000.

them to continue to open even larger stores with more selection at lower prices.

Since they are focused on only one type of merchandise, they attract employees who are interested in the product category itself. Plus, most category-busters hold on-site classes for employees and for customers interested in learning more about their products. Category-busters often know more than manufacturers about their products and how consumers use them.

This knowledge, coupled with the extreme buying and marketing power of the category-busters, has led to a new phenomenon in retailing: Custom packaged, brand-name merchandise that is retail-priced below average-unit manufacturing cost. In effect, retail goods priced below wholesale.

Here's one example of how this arrangement works.

In 1992, a particular company sold a tool air compressor for $300 wholesale (200,000 units per annum) that retailed for $600 at high-end hardware and tool shops. The company manufactured this item for $200 per unit—$50 in variable labor and materials and $150 in five-year-amortized design, tool and die costs. To make a five-year production run of one million units, it had to spend $150 million up front ($150 per unit) on the plant, research, tool dies, engineering design, etc.

In 1993, Home Depot hypothesized that at a much lower retail price than $600, say $200 retail, it could sell 500,000 units of this product. Home Depot offered to purchase 500,000 units—but for $100 each. At first the company scoffed, stating that it cost them twice this price just to make them. But, after reflection, the company realized that the offer would technically be profitable for them on a marginal basis, and, if they didn't accept the offer, Home Depot would take it to a competitor who could build a higher volume plant and put them out of business. They accepted, and Home Depot actually ended up selling 800,000 units the first year. Subsequently, the manufacturer used the higher volume (now 1,000,000 units per year) to retool and lower their fixed costs to less than $50 per unit—far below the initial $150 per unit.

The ultimate beneficiary of this story was the consumer who was, and still is, able to purchase a $600-value product for only $200.[44]

Similar innovations, like purchasing the slow- or down-time of many manufacturers, are allowing both category-busters and innovative mass-merchants to continually sell top quality goods below wholesale.

For example, certain stores like Costco don't carry any specific items on a continual basis. Costco gives open orders to name-brand manufacturers that are typically filled when their manufacturing plants have idle time. Since the manufacturer had to pay for labor and overhead anyway during these time periods, it accepts these orders at far less than normal wholesale cost. Moreover, manufacturers are typically required to take back (including freight) any items not sold in a short time period, so Costco is assured it gets only the most fashionable, top-quality merchandise.

These and so many other examples work because of a profound change taking place on the economic landscape.

---

[44]Home Depot has since "institutionalized" such innovation by requiring existing vendors to submit a plan annually on how they will lower costs, or increase quality, by 20 percent per annum. If the existing vendor cannot meet these guidelines, their entire relationship is opened to competitive bidding by other vendors. This forces the manufacturers to innovate on a continual rather than on a "when-it's-too-late" basis.

***We are entering the era of effectively zero-
marginal production and physical distribution
costs.***

This statement has enormous implications for
every supplier and retailer.

The per-unit price of raw materials and
automated labor has fallen so low that the amortized
per-unit research and development (R&D) cost, plus
the amortized per-unit marketing cost, are almost all
that matters for many types of goods.

The pipeline from raw materials to finished
products travels through four stages:

(1) Research and development (R&D);

(2) Physical manufacturing or production;

(3) Intellectual distribution; and

(4) Physical distribution.

Traditionally, the largest component costs in
products and services were in variable per-unit (2)
physical manufacturing costs and (4) physical
distribution costs. Expensive raw materials and hand
labor made up the bulk of manufacturing expenses
and went up or down almost directly with each unit
(or 1,000 units) produced. Similarly, the physical
distribution costs of storing, transferring and
delivering the finished product made up the bulk of
distribution expenses, and also went up or down
almost directly with each unit (or 1,000 units)
distributed.

But today, most of the expense in making
products and services are in (1) research and
development costs and (3) intellectual distribution
costs. This applies almost 100 percent to new
products and services like software, entertainment
and communications—products whose costs are

almost entirely composed of R&D and marketing expenses. And it even applies to traditional physical products and services like cameras, clothes and other consumer items.

Thus, the nature of the opportunity in manufacturing and in distribution is changing— particularly for products with low marginal manufacturing or physical distribution cost. The opportunity in manufacturing is now in the design or invention of the product, rather than in finding a way to simply lower the per-unit cost of physical production. And the opportunity in distribution is now in intellectual distribution versus physical distribution.

The mass-merchants are the first retailers to feel this change. Millions of consumers are discovering how much more efficient it is to purchase their household consumables online or via some type of automatic direct factory-to-home replenishment system. In addition to lower prices resulting from bulk buying and from direct shipment from the manufacturer, the cost of physical delivery from UPS is often lower than the time and mileage cost for consumers to lug these items home themselves.

And these initial savings are just the beginning. As millions more consumers embrace direct delivery of household consumables, manufacturers will eventually ship the bulk of their produce directly to homes rather than stock items at intermediate waypoints like mass-merchants. Increased volume will drive prices down even further.

Anticipating this trend, we built our family residence with an enclosed glass-door front porch so delivery people could leave items when no one was home—it has a refrigerator, heater, a hanging rod for dry cleaning, and an electronic camera that takes a picture when someone is present. Such "electronic butler" areas, perhaps with magnetic card access, should eventually become standard household fixtures.

At the beginning of the twentieth century, railroads dominated the national physical distribution of manufactured goods and raw materials. The railroads disappeared because they saw their business as the railroad industry versus the transportation industry—and thus failed to capitalize on their customer relationships and make the transition from rail cars to trucks. Several mass-merchants are determined not to make this same mistake.

Wal-Mart, Costco and other merchants that specialize in physical distribution are rapidly building cyberstores like Wal-mart.com and Costco.com. They hope to beat the technological clock that threatens to put them out of business. But they are fighting an uphill battle because they are collectively still focused on a shrinking component of overall cost: physical distribution. For now and the foreseeable future, the greatest retailing opportunities will be in intellectual distribution.

New products and services have always required one-on-one customer education that only a trained user of the product itself can provide—the "high touch" needed with "high-tech." Some of these items were VCRs in the 1970s, discounted long-distance service and telephone answering machines in the 1980s, and better vitamins and nutritional foods in the 1990s.

Every year for the past few decades, more and more of the consumer dollar has been spent on such "new" products and services. Yet even including the recent growth of the category-busters, there have been fewer places each year for the consumer to go to learn that such products exist, let alone how to use them.

This required combination of high touch along

with high tech in new products accounts for much of the growth of person-to-person direct-selling companies—particularly in areas of new technology.

In the 1980s, Amway distributors launched consumer discount long-distance telephone service through an arrangement with MCI, as well as home-based electronic voice messaging through Amway's proprietary Amvox service.

In the 1990s, the most successful vitamin and nutritional supplement products were launched through direct-selling companies. Many popular categories of supplement products, like ephedra (weight loss), pycnogenol (antioxidant) and echinacea (colds and flu), were only available through direct-selling companies before they became off-the-shelf store products.

Led by nutritional products and new technology, sales of direct-selling companies in the U.S. alone rose 50 percent recently, from approximately $18 billion in 1995 to $27 billion in 1999. This was almost twice the sales growth rate of traditional retail stores during a similar period.[45]

But direct-selling companies have a long growth curve ahead of them before they reach the saturation now being experienced by the mass-merchants. Annual U.S. direct-selling sales of approximately $30 billion still amount to less than 1 percent of the more than $3 trillion ($3,000 billion) in sales at traditional U.S. retail stores. The sales of just one mass-merchant, Wal-Mart, exceeded $165 billion in 2000.

Some direct-selling companies themselves don't fully understand their own business. They still refer to end-users of their product as "customers" to whom they sell, versus "clients" whom they educate. The

---

[45]U.S. retail sales increased 27 percent from $2,359 billion in 1995 to $2,995 billion in 1999. (*Statistical Abstract of the United States, 1999*. U.S. Census Bureau.)

dictionary defines a "customer" as "one who purchases a commodity or service," versus a "client" who is defined as "a person who engages the professional advice or services of another."[46]

Despite the growth of both direct-selling companies and category busters, each year the backlog of unused, more efficacious consumer products continues to grow. For every household that starts using a better consumer product, from the latest digital camera to educational software to healthier foods and nutritional supplements, there seem to be dozens of new products and services that consumers haven't yet learned even exist.

Teaching consumers about such products and services, or intellectual distribution, is the greatest entrepreneurial opportunity now and for the foreseeable future.

*   *   *

We noted earlier that distribution costs had risen in the past three decades from about 50 percent to about 70 percent today of retail prices, and that the greatest fortunes have been made by people who found better ways of distributing things versus better ways of making things. But let's now examine more closely how these distribution pioneers were able to accomplish their goals.

By using electronic real-time communication to connect retailers and producers with their suppliers, companies like Wal-Mart were able to lower their distribution costs while actually improving customer service—delivering just what their customers wanted, when and where they wanted it. Incidentally, the

---

[46]*Merriam-Webster Collegiate Dictionary*, ©1996 Zane Publishing, Inc. and Merriam-Webster, Inc.

capacity today of Wal-Mart's computer database is second only to that of the Pentagon.[47]

At the beginning of the 1990s this just-in-time technology was generally limited to large companies that could afford to establish proprietary communication lines between themselves and the mainframe computers of their suppliers. This helped ignite the fire of economic expansion we are enjoying today. But then, in 1995, a historic decision was made that has had the effect of pouring gasoline on this fire.

The Internet of today was technically started in the 1960s by Pentagon weapons researchers, who sought to develop a system of communication that could survive the most catastrophic nuclear holocaust. This system was designed to connect disparate locations in a manner such that there was no one central processing location—and thus the surviving systems could continue indefinitely regardless of how many others were destroyed.[48]

It is this distinct feature, treating every sender and every receiver as a unique client/server or mainframe unto itself, that has allowed the Internet to evolve into the incredible *democratizer* it is today—

---

[47]Although he is rarely remembered that way, Sam Walton was really the first information-age CEO. After starting his company in 1962 at the age of 44, Walton attended an IBM school in computers in 1966 with the goal of hiring the smartest person in the class.

[48]It is fascinating to note, almost theologically, what happened when the Pentagon hired three different groups to begin working on the concept of the Internet in the early 1960s—at MIT, at Rand, and in the United Kingdom (at NPL). When they all came together in Washington to agree on a standard in 1968, they had all come to the same conclusion regarding packets and independent client/servers, even though they had all proceeded under strict security guidelines and without ever knowing of each other's work.

changing the focus of world and economic power from the organization to the individual.

The first node on the Internet was installed in 1969 at UCLA, connecting computers on a network at UCLA with another computer at Stanford Research Institute. Two more nodes were soon added at UC–Santa Barbara and the University of Utah. This original Pentagon-funded net, called ARPANET, quickly grew to connect thousands of scientists and universities around the globe. A new standard for communication, called TCP/IP for short, was implemented in 1983.

Although funded by various government agencies originally to connect only defense-related scientists, in 1985 a decision was made to give access to all qualified users on campus access regardless of their academic discipline. This led to a nine-year program to privatize the backbone communication lines of the Internet—the backbone being the high-speed communication lines that connected one university's private network with another. By the time this privatization was accomplished, the Internet had grown to over 50,000 networks on all seven continents and outer space—and yet, the future hadn't really started for the Internet as we know it today.

In 1995 the historic decision was made to allow individual users the ability to obtain their own Internet accounts, ones independent of their university or organization.

Overnight, the economic and lifestyle benefits of instant real-time communication became available to everyone—leveling the playing field from the smallest entrepreneur to the largest *Fortune* 500 company. Companies that had already built their own proprietary communication systems now found themselves having to start over, since consumers (their ultimate customers), as well as thousands of smaller suppliers, were all going to be on the Internet themselves.

The results of this decision are just beginning to be felt on Main Street, from the act of waiting for a bus to shopping for food. Bus stop shelters will be electronically connected so that drivers only pull off the road only when passengers are waiting. Shoppers with electronically connected pantry closets will find their basket of replenishables (e.g., paper towels, milk, eggs) already pulled, loaded and waiting for them when they arrive at the supermarket, or automatically delivered to their homes.

But the results of this decision have already been felt on Wall Street, where the smart money has already anticipated what is about to occur on Main Street.

Today the majority of the companies with the largest market capitalization's (i.e., net worth) on any Top 10 or Top 100 Wall Street list are the high-technology "toolmakers." Toolmaker companies don't produce a single product that can feed, house, clothe, transport, heal, teach, inform or do anything else that a consumer might ultimately want.

Instead, toolmakers make products that help other companies that *do* produce these ultimate consumer wants do their job better—so much better that the toolmaker companies have become worth more than their customers (because of their value-added ability).[49] A glance at five of the ten highest valued companies in the U.S. stock market includes Cisco, Microsoft, Intel, Oracle and Vodaphone— companies that effectively didn't exist 20 years ago

---

[49]Or to put it another way, the majority of the economic value or cost in finished goods today is in the tools used to make them— rather than in their traditional labor and raw material costs.

[50]Kaufman, Leslie, "As Biggest Business, Wal-Mart Propels Changes Elsewhere," *New York Times*, October 22, 2000.

but whose combined net worth today exceeds $1 trillion.

This is the most misunderstood part of "dot-com" companies today: These and thousands of other technology-based companies are toolmakers. They do not produce end-use products desired by consumers—instead, they help other companies that do produce and distribute end-use products lower their costs and better serve their customers.

But eventually, the companies that do produce and distribute end-use products or services will have the final say—especially those which are the biggest customers of the toolmakers. At the beginning of 2001, Wal-Mart became the largest company in the United States, in both sales and number of employees.[50] For as John Maynard Keynes once said, "Consumption is the sole end of all economic activity."

Thus, the *explosive growth of today's economy is based fundamentally on using information-processing technology to dramatically reduce the cost of existing goods and services.* This is reflected in the high valuations placed today on our Internet companies, which are at the forefront of this task. As these companies succeed over the next few years and achieve these great efficiencies for their customers, consumers will continue to experience dramatic increases in their disposable income. The question, and opportunity for the wellness industry, is how they will choose to spend their escalating wealth.

*   *   *

In reviewing the history of distribution and examining the recent success of vehicles focused on intellectual distribution, the most obvious things missing are sickness and wellness industry distributors.

As previously noted, the sickness or medical industry occupies about one-seventh of our national economy. Yet where are the mass-merchants, the efficient service providers, and the category-busters for medical supplies? And even when we examine the direct-selling companies, many of which are focused on wellness and sickness products, why do they amount to such a minuscule part of the overall $1.4 trillion spent annually on U.S. sickness?

The reason is that the medical industry is mostly funded in the United States by the federal government—either 100 percent directly through payment mechanisms disguised as insurance programs like Medicare or Medicaid, or 50 percent indirectly through employee-subsidized health insurance programs. This federal subsidy is responsible for the byzantine insurance and payment structure in the sickness industry that limits competition and consumer choice.

In the next two chapters we will examine how sickness is funded today, and how both the sickness and the wellness industries will be funded tomorrow. What we will see is the coming breakdown of the corporate health insurance monopoly, and with it the emergence of real consumer choice for families in making their own sickness and wellness decisions.

Chapter 6

Sickness Insurance

You load sixteen tons and what do you get?
Another day older and deeper in debt.
Saint Peter, don't you call me 'cause I can't go,
I owe my soul to the company store.

"Sixteen Tons," Merle Travis (1946)

Today millions of Americans owe their soul to the *company doctor.* Most employees cannot afford private health insurance, and even among those who can, many have a family member with a preexisting medical condition. Like indentured servants in olden times, these Americans cannot change jobs, or even quit and strike out on their own, because they cannot obtain affordable medical care for their families from anywhere except their current employer.

The U.S. federal government is primarily responsible for this new form of economic slavery. Current income tax laws subsidize 50 percent or more of a family's medical costs *only* if they obtain their medical care from their employer. This massive federal tax subsidy has preempted the private sector from developing affordable direct-to-consumer health insurance plans that serve individual needs. It is also indirectly responsible for the continued focus of our current health insurance system on sickness rather than on wellness—paying for the treatment of symptoms of disease rather than for their prevention or their cure.

Moreover, another byproduct of this nineteenth century servile system, escalating medical costs, threatens to bankrupt many companies and even the entire economy, given the fact that doctors and patients consume mostly *other people's money* when making their decisions.

The $1.4 trillion Americans currently spend on sickness is growing much faster than the U.S. Gross Domestic Product (GDP)—it is expected to more than double by 2010 and, if current trends continue unchecked, will exceed the GDP itself by 2050. Its fallout could make the $200 billion savings and loan disaster of the 1980s pale by comparison—tens of millions of Americans could lose their life savings to medical expenses. Despite a steadily rising economy in the last decade, U.S. personal bankruptcy filings doubled—from approximately 750,000 in 1990 to 1.5 million in 1999—with much of the increase resulting from family medical catastrophes.

Fortunately, change is under way. And there is great opportunity for wellness-oriented individuals to profit from the coming chaos. But in order to navigate through the icy waters ahead and to take advantage of these opportunities, it is first necessary to understand how company-paid medical care works and how it became ubiquitous in the first place.

As noted in Chapter Four, individual U.S. federal marginal income tax rates rose throughout the twentieth century, reaching peak rates of 92–94 percent by 1964 before stabilizing at 70 percent until the 1980s. In some states in the 1950s, some taxpayers actually experienced marginal income tax rates above 100 percent—that is, they had to pay more than $1 in income taxes for each additional $1 they earned.[51] (Today most U.S. high-earning individuals pay about 50 percent of their income in just federal and state income taxes—not including

---

[51]This occurred because a single additional dollar in income could push some taxpayers into a higher bracket on all of their income.

property taxes, sales taxes, gasoline taxes, etc.)

Because most raises to high-earning business executives would have ended up in the pockets of the federal government, businesspeople lobbied Congress in the 1950s for the right to receive tax-free perks like medical care for their families, paid for by their employers. Congress obliged, and almost overnight company-paid medical care became a standard perk for business executives. Then, in the 1960s, because of the enormous federal tax subsidy on this benefit, unions demanded company-paid medical care in lieu of some wage increases. By the 1970s the concept of having your healthcare paid for by your employer was universal.

Originally, companies thought of this as a great way to compensate employees with the federal government paying about half the cost. However, it soon grew into the cost-escalating, out-of-control system we have today, where almost everyone (except the elderly and poor) receives their healthcare benefits from an employer—probably the last entity people would like to have involved in their personal medical care if they had a choice.

Today, under a qualified medical plan, employers are allowed a 100 percent corporate income tax deduction for medical insurance premiums, and employees do not report receiving these medical benefits when they pay their income taxes. This system is terribly unfair: Americans working for large corporations get up to 50 percent or more of their medical costs paid (indirectly) by the federal government; while the working poor, the self-employed, and the unemployed have to earn up to $2 before income taxes in order to have $1 (or less) to spend on medical care.[52] Either everyone should

---

[52]We will soon examine new tax regulations taking full effect in 2003 that will begin to level the playing field for some self-

receive tax-deductible healthcare or no one should.

Moreover, because the subsidy is in the form of a tax deduction versus a tax credit, rich individuals receive much higher subsidies than lesser income taxpayers. And because the subsidy comes in the form of a complex set of tax regulations, it is easily manipulated by large medical insurance and pharmaceutical companies seeking to protect their profits.

For example, when it comes to treating depression, the U.S. federal tax code allows a tax deduction for the purchase of expensive prescription drugs (like Prozac) but does not allow the same deduction if the consumer elects to treat his or her depression with a safer and cheaper nonprescription remedy like St. John's wort.[53] The Internal Revenue Service should not be telling consumers what drugs to take or not to take for their ailments.

As medical costs have spiraled upward, corporations providing healthcare benefits have focused mostly on cutting costs for existing services rather than on providing innovative new products that consumers want, like wellness services and alternative medicine. These cost-cutting efforts have often used their great bargaining power against healthcare professionals.

Today almost every physician, pharmacy, hospital and healthcare provider operates under a labyrinthine payment system designed to extract the most out of the people who can afford the least.

---

employed individuals.

[53]IRS Rev. Rul. 68-433, 1968-2 CB 110, says that insurance premiums for the reimbursement of prescription drugs only qualifies as a health insurance expense. Of course, some savvy pharmaceutical firms get around this regulation by making much more expensive "prescription" versions of their over-the-counter products.

Here's how this system works:

A physician might competitively set the price for an individual service or office visit at $75. A large employer or healthcare insurer, representing half of her existing patients, negotiates a lower price for its employees of $55—typically a 15–35 percent discount off the standard rate. The physician has no choice but to oblige this request and seek to make up her losses by raising the $75 set price to $95 for her other patients. Over time, as multiple large players (generally through preferred purchasing organizations, or PPOs) enter the marketplace, a multitiered system emerges with different patients being charged four to five different prices for the exact same item or service.

It is a credit to their profession that most medical professionals still seek to provide the same level of service to each patient regardless how much they are being paid. But, among some cost-strapped professionals, a new form of appointment-rationing has begun where the patient with the highest-paying PPO gets the first available appointment (encouraging the lesser-paying PPO patient to go elsewhere or forgo the service entirely).[54]

Besides being terribly unfair, this byzantine system creates irrational consumption decisions on the part of consumers and providers. As the price paid by the consumer and received by the doctor bears less and less relation to actual cost, the free market is not allowed to work its economic magic. Doctors overutilize services for which they get higher reimbursement, and patients underutilize services priced artificially high, to the detriment of themselves

---

[54]Patients with cash or without PPOs sometimes never get appointments, since it is mostly assumed that they cannot afford to pay anything at all.

and their children.

But the biggest problem with our current medical care insurance system, where more than 90 percent of expenses are paid by someone *other than* the patient and the doctor deciding on the treatment, is that it is focused on paying for the treating of the symptoms of illness rather than on preventing illness.

This is partly because, as previously mentioned, it is more profitable for medical companies to produce products that create customers for life—products that treat symptoms rather than products focused on cures or prevention. But it is mostly because the third parties paying for the medical treatment—the insurance companies and ultimately the employers—do not have a financial stake in the long-term health of their employees.

Employees used to stay with their employers for 25 years or more. Today, the average employee is projected to change jobs ten times over his or her 45-year working life. Most of the major illnesses on which one can spend $1 today to save $100 tomorrow, like heart disease from obesity or cancer from poor nutrition, will not show up until the employee is long gone or retired—at which time the $100 cost is picked up by another employer or by taxpayers through Medicare.

As medical costs have escalated, employers have, in effect, told their medical insurance companies to pay only for expenses related to keeping or getting the insured back to work—and certainly not to pay for the prevention of a disease that will not manifest itself during the expected tenure of the employee with the company. Weight reduction, nutritional advice, vitamins, minerals, smoking cessation, and hundreds of other wellness-related or preventative treatments are excluded from almost all corporate- and government-sponsored medical plans.

This causes even greater escalation in medical costs. Most physicians I interviewed believe that the majority of nongeriatric medical expenses are caused by just poor diet and smoking—something they are effectively limited from treating in the current PPO or HMO[55] environment.

Let's examine a typical situation where a 100-employee U.S. company provides medical benefits at an annual group premium cost of $500,000 per annum ($5,000 per employee or family)

If the employer wanted the employees to purchase the same medical insurance themselves, even if it was available for purchase directly at $5,000 per annum per family, it would cost about twice as much. This employer would have to pay up to $10,000 in wages and withholding taxes in order for each employee to have this same $5,000 after taxes available to buy medical insurance themselves. This represents an immediate cash savings of $5,000 per employee—or put another way, an immediate cash cost to other U.S. taxpayers of $5,000 per employee. It's easy to see why most working Americans today receive their medical insurance through their employers, and why employer-paid medical insurance premiums exceed $600 billion per annum.

The concept of insurance works because of the mathematical "law of large numbers." In order to provide insurance for a catastrophic medical occurrence, the insurance company relies on fact that there will be a large enough pool of people paying premiums so that the extraordinary costs of the unhealthy few can be borne by the healthy many. Each corporate group of employees is considered to be a separate pool for insurance underwriting

---

[55]In a health maintenance organization (HMO) the provider is paid a flat annual amount per patient versus being paid for each service rendered.

purposes.

Now assume that one of the employees, or one of their children, develops a chronic disease like diabetes or gets permanently injured in an automobile accident—a condition that allows the employee to continue working but ends up costing $100,000 in recurring annual medical expenses for drugs and treatment. Initially, the employer's insurance company bears this $100,000 expense, but next year it will raise the employer's $500,000 annual premium to $600,000 or more to cover this now-anticipated additional expense (as well to try and recoup its prior loss).[56] The employer is free to shop around for a different insurance provider, but is unlikely to find a better deal since the main criterion used to underwrite and price a group policy is the prior year's medical expenses of that group.

The employer and the employee are both trapped.

The employer needs to get rid of the employee to lower its total group medical insurance premium, but under federal law it cannot fire someone for medical reasons who is still "doing their job." Fortunately for the employer but unfortunately for the employee, a person with a chronic medical condition, or a very sick child, is unlikely to be able to continue "doing their job."

In the event that the employee is still capable of doing his or her job, often by putting in extra hours, the employee cannot quit as most new employers will not hire them—unless the $100,000 in anticipated annual medical expenses for the preexisting condition are excluded from their medical insurance

---

[56]Many states limit the ability of insurance carriers to raise premiums for "small employers" (generally 50 employees or less) due to high-loss experience, or limit the size of such premium increases to be within predefined "rating bands" for small employee groups.

coverage.[57] It is estimated that of the 187 millions Americans receiving healthcare benefits from employers, approximately 22 percent, more than 41 million people, have some preexisting health condition in their family limiting their ability to get healthcare coverage from a new employer or insurance company.[58]

To ease the short-term burden on terminated employees, and perhaps to ease the consciences of the employers who were forced to terminate them, Congress passed the Consolidated Omnibus Reconciliation Act (COBRA) in 1986. COBRA mandates that terminated employees should be able to purchase health insurance from their former employer for up to 18 months after their employment ends, at a premium not to exceed 102 percent of the group rate. And after 18 months, some states require that former employees with COBRA become automatically eligible for individual policies. But while COBRA and such individual policies generally

---

[57]Technically, the federal Health Insurance Portability and Accountability Act of 1996 (HIPAA) limits insurance companies from excluding most preexisting conditions on new employees provided that, among other things, the individual employee was covered for this condition at a prior employer and has not had a lapse in healthcare coverage for more than 63 days. HIPAA has created a "cat and mouse" game where insurance companies do their best to get a group policyholder to drop their policy while technically following HIPAA and other federal regulations. For example, HIPAA requires insurance companies offering individual policies to accept former-group applicants, but does not specify at what rates. Insurance companies offering individual policies typically get approval for a high-rated, extremely expensive policy that few could afford, and then, in order to comply with HIPAA, "offer" this too-expensive policy to HIPAA applicants with preexisting conditions.

[58]This 22-percent figure is from verbal estimates I have culled while interviewing insurance executives and brokers. There are

cover preexisting conditions, few terminated
employees can afford this insurance, especially
without the income tax advantages they used to get
when their insurance was paid for by their employer.
Only approximately 21 percent of terminated eligible
employees elect to purchase COBRA insurance.[59]
Moreover, the COBRA program implicitly assumes
that the employee will find another job providing
health insurance before the end of this 18-month
period. Few with preexisting chronic medical
conditions probably do.

Similarly, the Health Insurance Portability and
Accountability Act of 1996 (HIPAA) was enacted by
Congress to limit insurance companies from
excluding coverage for a preexisting condition to new
employees if the employee was covered for such a
condition by a prior employer. However, among other
limitations, HIPAA does not apply if the employee has
had a lapse in coverage (e.g., he or she has been out
of work without COBRA) for more than 63 days.

As the company's pool of employees age over time,
more of them (or their dependents) will develop some
chronic condition that will raise the cost of the group

---

roughly 225 million people in the U.S. with health insurance
broken down as follows: 23 million Medicare (of which 80 percent
purchase supplemental policies); 15 million Medicaid; and 187
million employer. This 187 million figure consists of 40 million
with large corporations that self-insure, and 147 million with
large—and small businesses—that purchase third-party health
insurance (including 16 million with individual health insurance
purchased policies covering 24 million insured).

[59]A study completed six years after COBRA was passed showed
that 21 percent of workers who qualified elected COBRA
continuation coverage. (Mark C. Berger, Dan A. Black, Frank A.
Scott, Carolyn Looff and Associates, Health Insurance Coverage
of the Unemployed Final Report, April 17, 1996. Prepared for the
Pension and Welfare Benefits Administration, United States
Department of Labor, Washington, D.C.)

medical insurance premium and make them individually unemployable somewhere else. Moreover, the increased costs of these chronic conditions may eventually cause the employer to cut back on their medical benefits or even go out of business entirely—as they lose customers to competitors with younger, healthier, and thus less costly employees.

This is the most ironic part of the U.S. health insurance system today. *The people who feel the safest—individuals receiving health insurance through their employers—are actually the most at risk.* For many of them, it is only a question of time before they or one of their dependents develops a chronic condition. And even if this never occurs, it is only a question of time, in our rapidly changing technological world, before they find themselves out of work before age 65.[60]

When such people find themselves out of work before age 65, either through termination or early retirement, they often cannot obtain affordable individual medical insurance at any price—even if they don't have any preexisting conditions. There are several reasons this is so.

First, since the majority of Americans receive medical insurance or coverage from their employers, in many states there are simply not enough people left over to create a marketplace for affordable individual policies. Each individual health insurance policy must be separately approved by the insurance commissioner in each state. Even in larger states where there are enough potential applicants, insurance companies find it difficult to market profitably to, underwrite, and service individuals not

---

[60]U.S. citizens become eligible for Medicare at age 65, although in this case Medicare would not cover their under-65 dependents.

connected by a common employer (who typically has an on-site healthcare benefits administrator).

Second, employers naturally hire the most productive people and avoid or fire the ones who produce the least. In a nation where 61 percent of the population is overweight and 27 percent are clinically obese and unhealthy, those who don't get hired (or who do get fired) are often also the most unhealthy. Employers skim the cream off the top of the health insurance marketplace—leaving a disproportionate number of unhealthy people to the individual health insurance market. Insurers often automatically assume there is something wrong with anyone who doesn't already have health insurance, and underwrite individual applicants under much stricter standards than applicants in a group policy.

Third and most important, even when approved, individuals are charged more for the same benefits than applicants in a group policy. This occurs for several reasons—one of which is the number of laws that protect individual policyholders from having their premium raised (or their policy dropped) in the event that they or a dependent develop a chronic condition.

In the above example, where the individual employee (or his or her child) developed a chronic condition costing $100,000 per annum on an ongoing basis, the insurance company was allowed to raise the employer group premium to cover this anticipated future expense. If this same person had an individual versus a group health insurance policy, the insurance company would not be allowed to raise the premium or drop the insured from coverage.[61] In general, insurance companies may only legally raise

---

[61]Some states apply such individual premium protection to small (2–50) employer groups.

individual premiums equally for all types of individuals in a defined class (typically individuals residing in that state) rather than for specific persons with high claim experience.

Note that while this legislated protection can limit your ability to obtain an individual health insurance policy, as we will see in the next chapter, *it can be a great asset in structuring a long-term wellness-oriented solution to the health insurance dilemma.*

Several states have unsuccessfully tried to force insurers to offer individual health insurance. For example, the state of New York insists that insurance carriers offering group health insurance in their state also offer guaranteed-issue community-rated individual health insurance to all applicants. Guaranteed-issue means that the carrier is not allowed to consider, or even ask about, the health of the applicant or their dependents. Preexisting conditions must be covered after a maximum of six months, except for pregnancy and certain other conditions, which must be covered immediately. "Community-rated" means that the premium charged must be the same for all applicants, whether they be 18 years old in perfect health or 60 years old with a terminal illness.

The effect of these onerous regulations in New York (and the few other guaranteed-issue states[62]) is that insurance companies only offer individual policies there at extremely high cost (typically $800 per month for a family of three) or not at all, and discourage applications with practices such as refusing to pay outside agency commissions on individual policies. Savvy applicants and insurance

---

[62]Generally, the states requiring guaranteed-issue are New York, New Jersey, Massachusetts, Vermont, New Hampshire, Maine and Kentucky. Washington and Oregon recently repealed their guaranteed-issue requirements.

agents play a cat-and-mouse game to get around some of these restrictions. For example, pregnant women buy policies in their eighth month of pregnancy and cancel them after childbirth. Insurance agents form private open-enrollment "associations" or "unions," which are really vehicles disguised to sell marked-up restrictive group coverage to individuals and create commissions for the agents, disguised as "dues."

For the past 20 years, I and several other economists have argued in the White House and in Congress about the unfairness of only allowing corporate employees tax-deductible health insurance and its detrimental effects on our entire healthcare insurance and delivery system. Congress has begun to listen.

Thanks to recent legislation, *in 2001 self-employed individuals may deduct from their taxable income 60 percent of the amount they spend on health insurance premiums for themselves, their spouses and their dependents.*[63] *This figure rises to 70 percent in 2002 and to 100 percent in 2003 and beyond.*[64]

This, coupled with recent legislation allowing medical savings accounts on an experimental basis and other new medical income tax deductions—which we will also examine in the next chapter—is the crack in the wall of the corporate sickness insurance monopoly.

---

[63]A self-employed individual (as defined in Code Sec. 401[c][1]) may deduct as a business expense a statutory percentage of the amount paid for medical insurance on himself, his spouse and his dependents (Code Sec. 162[l][1]).

[64]Noting that large corporations have always been allowed to deduct 100 percent, Congress passed H.R. 2488, the Taxpayer Refund and Relief Act of 1999, which would have allowed immediate 100 percent deductibility for self-employed businesses. It was vetoed by then-President Clinton.

No one yet has any idea of how efficient, and even how enjoyable, shopping for wellness (and sickness) services might be if consumers were given the ability to choose freely among competitive cost-effective providers, but we are about to find out.

Approximately 50 million people in the United States are either self-employed or have some part of their income derived from self-employment. By 2003, many of these individuals will be allowed to freely purchase part or all of their medical care on almost an economic parity basis with large corporations.[65] These astute consumers will comprise the first major group spending their own versus someone else's money on healthcare.

Moreover, many of these individuals with self-employment income live in households with traditional corporate- or government-sponsored medical benefit plans. Competitive forces will eventually force these traditional providers to allow their customers also to choose the wellness and sickness products that they desire, versus the products and services forced upon them by cost-cutting corporate employers and lobbyist-controlled government medical plans.

No one knows how innovative and efficient we might become if we got the federal government out of the healthcare business and applied "Yankee ingenuity" to the distribution side of our healthcare system. But when we look at the growth of so many other industries—like food service, transportation, and consumer electronics—we begin to get an idea of what might be possible.

Food service outside of the home used to be either a dull cafeteria or a much more expensive restaurant.

---

[65]IRS code limits the Self-Employed Health Insurance Deduction to Net Earned Income (there is no such limitation for corporations paying health insurance premiums).

Through innovative technology, the restaurant industry lowered its prices and increased its product offerings so much that the demand for its product increased 1,000 percent—from 1950 to 2000, Americans went from eating 5 percent to 50 percent of their meals outside of the home. Fifty years ago a child's "Can we go out to dinner?" was met with "What do think we are—millionaires!" Today, such a request is usually met by "What kind of food do you want?" and dining out is an enjoyable and affordable experience for almost everyone.

Similar examples abound for air transportation, vacations, fashionable clothes, consumer electronics, and hundreds of other luxury services and products that people thought could never be made affordable on a mass-market basis.

The 50 million Americans who are self-employed, or have some part of their income derived from self-employment, will be the first customers of the greatest entrepreneurial opportunity of the twenty-first century—the wellness industry. In the next chapter we will further examine this opportunity and see how entrepreneurs can financially provide themselves and their families with such efficacious wellness (and sickness) products and services.

Chapter 7

Paying for Wellness

Why traditional healthcare will be expanded to cover wellness, how you can get wellness benefits now, and why the federal government will ultimately provide basic sickness coverage for everyone.

Most people have comprehensive insurance on their automobiles. Yet they don't file a claim with their car insurance company when they buy gasoline, have their car cleaned, replace the tires or brakes, or change the oil. Even if they have an accident they are typically 100 percent responsible for any costs below the "deductible" on their policy.

Most people have homeowner's insurance on their homes. Yet they don't file a claim with their property insurance company when they buy heating fuel, have their house painted, or install a new roof. And here, too, they typically have a deductible where the insured pays entirely any claim below $500 or $1,000 per event.

Any financial advisor will tell you that it is foolish to buy insurance covering an expense that you can comfortably afford to pay on your own. The cost of the paperwork involved on each transaction, plus the costs incurred by the insurance company in issuing and enforcing the policy, would cause the premiums to far exceed, over time, any potential benefits. Many consumers have discovered that they can save hundreds or thousands of dollars a year by raising the deductible on their automobile and homeowner policies.[66]

---

[66]Raising the deductible on an automobile policy from, say, $500

In homeowners, automobile, life and all other types of insurance except one, insurance is used to cover only those catastrophic expenses that the insured party cannot comfortably afford to pay on his or her own. In these cases, most of the premiums paid for insurance serve a valuable function for the insured and his or her family.

In health insurance, most of the premiums paid do not serve a similarly valuable function.

Most people have a health insurance policy with coverage for incidental maintenance expenses that healthcare consumers don't really need covered. In addition to being economically foolish, this coverage supports a byzantine distribution system and payment mechanism that wastes hundreds of billions each year.[67] Think for a moment of how inefficient it would be if you had to file a claim with your automobile insurance company every time you bought gasoline or changed your oil—or if you could only buy gas or have your car maintained at a particular service station where your insurance company had negotiated a discounted rate for such services.

Think how difficult it would be if you had to get approval from your homeowner's insurance company to pay utility bills, or change your carpets, or paint your house—and if you could only purchase such items from a store selected by your insurance

---

to $1,000 often reduces the annual premium by $500 or more—the insured typically pockets the $500 per annum and only loses out if he or she has more than one major accident per year on a regular basis. The only ones who definitely lose in such a situation are the insurance agents—who are paid a percentage of the total premium and sometimes paid lesser percentages on less-profitable products like high-deductible insurance.

[67]Approximately 20 percent of healthcare insurance premiums go toward overhead.

company, and only purchase certain types of carpet or paint colors that your insurance company had preapproved.

Think of how much lower the prices are, and better the selection is, at the mass-merchants and category-busters ranging from Home Depot to PetsMart to Office Max—and think how none of these retailers would exist if the consumer were not free to shop competitively in each of these areas.

When you stop and think about it, it doesn't take long to see how inefficient we are in distributing medical products and services, and what great opportunities are probably being missed. But our medical services distribution system actually looks efficient when compared to our medical services insurance and payment system.

If you contacted your health insurance company today and told them that from now on you would like to pay the first, say, $2,500 a year in your family's medical expenses, they would probably lower your annual premium by $3,000 or more. This puts you ahead by $500 per annum even if you had a medical catastrophe in your family.

That is correct—almost any health insurance company would gladly lower your annual premium by $3,000 or more if you agreed to raise your annual deductible by $2,500. Here's why.

When you incur a $50 expense at a doctor or other medical service provider, your insurance company incurs an expense of $75 or more—$50 to pay the doctor and at least $25 for the paperwork and overhead required by the transaction. This is one of the reasons insurance companies have been pushing their insured to enroll in health maintenance organizations (HMOs) where the provider is paid a flat annual amount per patient (capitation) versus being paid for each service rendered.

On average, health insurance companies spend about 20 percent on overhead, but this average number is misleading. To approve and pay a single $10,000 hospital bill it might cost an insurance company only $500 (5 percent) in transaction costs—dealing with the hospital and cutting them a check. But to approve and pay a $50 medical bill from a single provider might cost the insurance company $25 (50 percent) or more in transaction costs—sometimes even more than the actual cost of the medical service itself.

The first $2,500 or so of a family's annual medical expenses are typically spent in $50 to $125 increments in 20 to 30 different transactions. No wonder your insurance company might lower your annual premium by 120 percent of the increase in your annual deductible. Most, in fact, already have, by incorporating this 120 percent or greater reduction into their published rates.

For example, in 2001, Blue Cross–Blue Shield of Utah offered a zero-deductible individual health policy for $415 per month, or $4,980 per year (two parents age 35 with three healthy children). The premium for this same policy with a $2,500 deductible was $159 per month, or $1,908 per annum—a $3,072 (123 percent) annual reduction in premium for a $2,500 increase in the annual deductible.

Blue Cross–Blue Shield Health Insurance Policy
Two Parents (age 35) and three children

Annual Deductible	Annual Premium
$ - 0 -	$4,980
$2,500	$1,908
Savings	$3,072

Moreover, with this particular policy as with most major medical high-deductible policies nationwide, the insured still participates in the insurance company's preferred provider organization (PPO) network for expenditures below the $2,500 deductible—getting the 15–35 percent negotiated discounts even though the insured pays for these transactions themselves.[68]

But most important of all, about 78 percent of the people with employer-paid health insurance do not spend anywhere near $2,500 per annum on medical care—this 78 percent would be simply reducing their annual medical insurance cost from $4,980 to their new $1,908 annual premium plus a few hundred dollars for incidentals like annual checkups and cold remedies. Overall, about 70 percent of the U.S. population spends $150 or less per annum on medical expenses.[69]

So why, then, if the insurance companies already offer such 120 percent or greater price reductions for high-deductible policies, do most people still have zero- or low-deductible policies—policies where the paperwork costs of the service provided sometimes exceeds the price of the actual service itself?

One reason is simply inertia on the part of employers and employees who purchase most private health insurance. Employers (wisely) don't put the time and talent into managing healthcare benefits that they do into managing their businesses. Moreover, since the days when most laborers worked at a plant with a company doctor, employees are used to getting a 100 percent medical benefit from their

---

[68]In fact, the insurance company typically requires the insured to utilize the PPO in order to keep a record of, and maintain an approval process for, the amounts spent under the deductible in case the $2,500 annual limit is reached.

[69]"Seventy percent of any population spends $150 or less on healthcare in a year," according to Mark Weinberg, Group President at California's Blue Cross unit, which covers 850,000 individuals. ("Consumers Facing Sharp Rise in Health Costs," *New York Times*, 10 December 2000.)

employers. Changes in healthcare benefits, even changes that benefit employees, are often met by employees with a "don't confuse me with the facts" attitude. This is particularly prevalent at the lower end of the employment spectrum where prospective hires compare medical benefits between companies almost as much as they compare the wages being offered.

Another reason that most people have such wasteful low- or no-deductible medical insurance policies is the United States tax code. If an employer raised the deductible in their group policy to $2,500 a year per employee or family, and agreed to pay employees any additional amounts they spend toward meeting their $500 deductible, these additional payments would not be tax-deductible— the company would have to pay employees about twice as much before state and federal taxes to net each employee the same amount.[70]

But the major reason that employers are not lining up to creatively structure higher deductible health insurance policies for their employees is that they are locked into providing health insurance for their entire group—including the 22 percent of employees who consume much more in medical expenses.

About 22 percent of employees with employer-paid health insurance, or one of their dependents, have a preexisting medical condition. If they were to

---

[70]Perspicacious healthcare benefits managers should be able to get around this income tax roadblock. The employer could pay the insurer $2,500 of the $3,000 saved in premiums per employee, and then request that the insurer simply automatically (without processing) pay any employee "under-deductible" claims up to $2,500 per annum. But, as we will see in a moment, this would not work in a group policy environment, since typically 22 percent of the employees would not qualify at all for high-deductible reduced-premium health insurance.

leave their current employer, this condition would hinder their ability to obtain a private individual health insurance policy or find employment (along with medical coverage) somewhere else. This unfortunate 22 percent utilize medical services far in excess of the typical $5,000 annual premium paid by their employer—they average about four times this amount ($20,000) per annum on a recurring basis. The insurance company only agrees to cover this 22 percent of employees because it is also receiving the $5,000 per annum premium on the 78 percent of healthier employees who incur almost no medical costs.

Health and life insurance originated with the eighteenth- and nineteenth-century "friendly societies" of the working classes—where the randomly fortunate "many" agreed to take care of the randomly unfortunate "few." This system implies that any single unidentifiable member of the group has an equal chance of being struck by the insured catastrophe. Today, in healthcare, this is no longer the case.

Today, when 27 percent of Americans are obese and 61 percent are overweight, the overwhelming majority of nongeriatric healthcare expenses are incurred by people easily identifiable by their weight or their smoking habits.

A wellness-oriented employee might be eager to give up part of his or her income for the child of a coworker struck randomly by leukemia. But, when given a choice, that same employee might not be eager to give up part of his or her income to treat hypertension in a coworker who is 100 pounds overweight due to gluttony, or lung disease in a coworker who refuses to quit smoking.

And thanks to recently passed U.S. legislation that is leveling the playing field between corporate- and self-employed individuals, this "choice" is becoming available for healthy wellness-oriented individuals. Individuals in the 78 percent group of employees without preexisting medical conditions can now drop the employer-based sickness insurance system before it drops them—opting out of the employer-paid health insurance monopoly.

This "choice" can save wellness-oriented individuals approximately $3,000 a year on their family's annual sickness insurance.

Yet these individuals will not simply pocket the savings. *Most will choose to invest it into what they hold dearest: their continued health and wellness.* They will use part of this $3,000, partly on a tax-deductible basis, to pay for vitamins, fitness clubs, minerals, weight control programs, and hundreds of other wellness-related or preventative treatments.

Let's examine how wellness-oriented individuals can redirect $3,000 per year of the $5,000 they (or their employer) pay for sickness insurance into current and future wellness products and services.

*   *   *

Consider the healthy family described above with the zero-deductible Blue Cross–Blue Shield policy costing $415 per month, or $4,980 annually. This family would change their policy to the $2,500-deductible one from Blue Cross–Blue Shield costing $159 per month, or $1,908 per annum—a $256-per-month, or $3,072, reduction in its annual premium. They would then contribute this $256 per month, or $3,072 per annum, in savings to what we'll call their "Wellness Savings Account™" or "Wellness Services Account™" (hereafter referred to as WSA™) that they would open at a local financial institution.[71]

---

[71]Wellness Savings Account, Wellness Services Account, and WSA are trademarks of Wellness Services, Inc. All rights reserved.

Each month the family would draw on its WSA for sickness expenses incurred below the $2,500 annual deductible amount, as well as for wellness products and services not typically covered by sickness insurance plans. Since most of these wellness purchases would not count toward the deductible, they should set up reserves of $2,500 as soon as possible. To facilitate withdrawals, the local financial institution would give them a VISA-type debit card and checkbook on the WSA account—the VISA debit card could also be the same PPO card they use to obtain discounted services in the Blue Cross–Blue Shield network.

During the first year with this program, they might spend $400 or so in medical expenses for annual physicals, spend $600 on wellness products and services, and put $2,072 reserves in their WSA to meet the annual deductible if a catastrophe arose.

Year One – Wellness Savings Account (WSA)

Beginning WSA Account Balance	$ 0
Interest Earned*	$ 82
Annual WSA Contribution	$3,072
Medical Expenses	$ (400)
Wellness Expenses	$ (600)
Ending WSA Account Balance	$2,154

*8% compounded monthly

The next year they would begin with last year's $2,154 surplus ($2,072 contribution plus $82 interest). Thus in Year 2 and beyond (holding constant their $400 per annum in medical expenses), they could spend up to $2672 per year on wellness products and services—all while still keeping a $2,500 minimum balance in their WSA to meet their annual deductible in the event of a medical emergency. However, let's assume for now that they continue to spend only $50 per month or $600 per annum on wellness—creating a $2,072 recurring annual surplus in their WSA that would soon accumulate to tens of thousands of dollars.

Year Two – Wellness Savings Account (WSA)

Beginning Initial WSA Account Balance	$2,154
Interest Earned*	$ 260
Annual WSA Contribution	$3,072
Actual Medical Expenses	$ (400)
Actual Wellness Expenses	$ (600)
Ending WSA Account Balance	$4,486

*8% compounded monthly

If this money was invested at 8 percent, in just ten years the accumulated surplus would exceed $31,000—the interest on which alone could fund the entire $1,908 annual premium—giving them effectively free medical insurance for the rest of their working lives. Or it could become a $31,000 nest egg to supplement Medicare or to leave to their children.

Year Ten – Wellness Savings Account (WSA)

Beginning Initial WSA Account Balance	$27,235
Interest Earned*	$ 2,343
Annual WSA Contribution	$ 3,072
Actual Medical expenses	$ (400)
Actual Wellness Expenses	$ (600)
Ending WSA Account Balance	$31,649

*8% compounded monthly

Theoretically, a healthy couple who averaged $400 a year in medical expenses could accumulate more than a quarter million dollars over a 30-year period:

Year 30 – Wellness Savings Account (WSA)

Beginning Initial WSA Account Balance	$236,084
Interest Earned*	$ 19,676
Annual WSA Contribution	$ 3,072
Actual Medical Expenses	$ (400)
Actual Wellness Expenses	$ (600)
Ending WSA Account Balance	$257,832

*8% compounded monthly

This scenario with WSAs is almost exactly what Congress had in mind when it passed legislation in 1997 authorizing medical savings accounts (MSAs) on an experimental basis. The "experiment" was scheduled to expire on December 31, 2000, but on December 21, 2000, Congress extended the deadline another two years until December 31, 2002. For individuals who take advantage of this legislation, the benefits of their MSA, and the right to make future contributions until age 65, are grandfathered for the rest of their lives.

Congress has allowed a maximum of 750,000 self-employed American taxpayers to open MSAs similar to the WSA account, but with one important difference: 100 percent of the contributions made to the MSA are tax-deductible. These contributions are deductible from adjusted gross income, meaning that self-employed individuals do not have to record a profit in order to get these tax benefits, just like large corporations, which are allowed unlimited tax deductions for medical insurance expenditures even if they don't make taxable income that year.[72]

The few hundred thousand fortunate individuals who open MSAs before January 31, 2002 are allowed to make tax-deductible contributions to their MSA of

---

[72]In such cases the medical insurance expense can be carried back or forward to other taxpaying years.

up to $3,600 (in year 2001, increased annually for inflation) each year until they reach age 65.[73] They can liberally make withdrawals to pay medical expenses from their MSA with a VISA-type debit card or checkbook—or they can just leave their money in their MSA to earn interest tax-free for future medical expenses. Coupled with the recent legislation allowing self-employed individuals tax deductions for health insurance premiums, beginning in 2003 these individuals will even be allowed a 100 percent tax deduction for the annual premium of their high-deductible policy. In cases of economic hardship, such as if they go on unemployment or COBRA, they are allowed to use their MSA tax-free to pay the premiums of their medical insurance policy.

And best of all, when they go on Medicare at age 65, the entire unspent amount in their MSA may be withdrawn for any purpose whatsoever with no penalties. Just like with an IRA, they pay income taxes then on only the amount withdrawn at their then-lower retirement tax bracket. But even better than an IRA, they pay no income taxes on amounts withdrawn to pay for medical expenses not covered by their Medicare or other health insurance.

The MSA is the ultimate vehicle when it comes to allowing individuals to make the right choices for themselves and their families. Individuals are allowed a tax deduction for almost all of their medical expenditures just as if they worked for a large corporation. Individuals decide themselves where to

---

[73]It is estimated that the single largest group of individuals opening MSAs to date have been physicians. Most insurance executives are surprised at the low number of taxpayers opening MSAs to date—these executives universally blamed the insurance brokerage community, noting that switching a family from a zero-deductible to a high-deductible policy typically reduces the brokerage commission from $850 (17 percent of $5000) to $340 (17 percent of $2000).

spend their money and are free to negotiate their own deals in the marketplace. Individuals get to keep any money they don't spend today to pay for medical expenses tomorrow, to fund their retirement, or to leave to their children. Even the interest earned over the years from the accumulating amounts in their MSA is tax-free (just like an IRA).

But most of all, individuals can make intelligent wellness investment decisions for their own continued health—weighing choices like the cost of vitamins and better nutrition today versus the cost of treating a disease later on.

Congress is examining the results of their MSA "experiment" that will now end on December 31, 2002. But the individuals who take advantage of the MSA opportunity will be enjoying the benefits of their MSA account, each year, for the rest of their lives.

I believe that Congress will soon make the MSA opportunity permanently available to all. They really have no choice, because the public already has spoken.

Between 1931 and 1976, federal law prohibited banks from paying interest on checking accounts. In 1976, a small savings bank in New England began offering interest on its checking accounts (calling it a savings account with checks versus a checking account with interest). The competition cried foul and demanded federal action. By the time the federal government got around to taking action, so many people had opened such accounts that the "action" taken by Congress was to pass laws legitimizing interest on all checking accounts.[74]

---

[74]Initially Congress passed a law authorizing such interest-bearing savings accounts, then called NOW Accounts (for Negotiable-Order-of-Withdrawal), for just the New England Federal Reserve District. The law was expanded to the rest of nation a few years later.

Similarly, for almost 50 years, federal law prohibited retailers from selling certain name-brand items below the manufacturer's list price. When Wal-Mart and other expanding retailers started ignoring these laws and discounting name brand items, the public response was so favorable that Congress was forced to abolish so-called "Fair Trade Laws" in 1975.

A hunting dog proudly marches in front of the hunters, keeping a watchful eye behind to make sure that it is being followed. If the hunters decide to go in the opposite direction, the dog sprints to a new place in front of them, again proudly proclaiming its place as their "leader."

Politicians today are like hunting dogs—carefully watching the latest poll to see in which direction the public wants to go, and then adopting this position as our "leader."

And today, one of the things people want most is more choices in how they spend their money on the sickness and wellness of their families.

But regardless of what Congress does in the near future in making the MSA option permanently available for self-employed individuals, there is no stopping WSA- or MSA-equivalent accounts. The laws and regulations prohibiting them are so vague, and so contrary to the public interest, that self-employed individuals and perspicacious entrepreneurs are now structuring MSA-type vehicles for themselves and for general public consumption. These wellness-oriented insurance products will be available for self-employed individuals and for the dependents of corporation employees whether or not Congress formally makes them permanently available.

*   *   *

If you derive all or some part of your income from self-employment, here are some of the regulations that exist for you to structure tax-advantaged wellness insurance for yourself and your family. These also apply to organizations seeking to offer tax-deductible wellness insurance for individuals with self-employed income.

Thanks to recent legislation, Section 162 of the Internal Revenue Code says that a self-employed individual can take a tax deduction only for medical insurance *premiums* for themselves, their spouse or their dependents.[75] This excludes amounts spent for medical expenses other than insurance premiums—such as amounts incurred for direct medical expenses below the deductible or outside the coverage of a health insurance policy.

But nowhere does the IRS code specifically define what "insurance" or a "premium" is, or limit the amount of medical reimbursements provided by the insurer receiving the tax-deductible premium.

An insurance company offering a $2,500-deductible policy could simply increase their annual premium by $2,500 per year and give the insured a VISA-type debit card and checkbook good for up to $2,500 in sickness or wellness expenses—with any unspent amounts each year accruing to the future benefit of the insured (similar to the cash-value increase in a whole-life insurance policy). The insured could have all the benefits of an WSA or MSA account—plus the purchasing power discounts of the insured PPO group made available *for wellness as well as sickness expenses.*

To ensure the tax deductibility of the premium, the insured would be individually responsible to see that this $2,500 went only to purchase IRS-approved tax-deductible medical expenses.

---

[75] 60 percent in 2001, 70 percent in 2002, and 100 percent in 2003 and beyond.

Where medical expenses (or reimbursements) are tax-deductible, IRS regulations generally allow any medical expense that is legitimately prescribed by a licensed physician. The tax courts have ruled that even luxury cruises qualify as tax-deductible medical expenses when prescribed by a doctor, and in some cases have also allowed a tax deduction for a spouse if it was necessary to accompany the "patient."

Many doctors would gladly issue "prescriptions" for weight-loss programs, fitness training, special vitamins and minerals, and all wellness-based products and services—especially if supplied with documentation demonstrating the medical efficacy of the requested item. The only reason they haven't issued such prescriptions up until now is that most of these items are available over-the-counter and not covered for reimbursement by company-sponsored medical insurance plans.

There are some minor exceptions to this general statement, such as a conflicting IRS revenue ruling that says that only insurance premiums covering prescription (versus over-the-counter) drugs qualify for tax-deductible medical expenses.[76] This ruling has been used (or abused) for years by large pharmaceutical firms who simply make more expensive "prescription" versions of their over-the-counter products—both to satisfy the IRS and to get employer-based medical insurance policies to pay for them.

If such wellness-oriented insurance was offered by a joint-venture between a wellness-supplier and an insurance company, the policy itself might only allow reimbursement for those wellness products and services deemed qualified and effective by the joint venture.

---

[76]IRS Rev. Rul. 68-433, 1968-2 CB 110.

The wellness supplier, seeking to qualify their products for insurance reimbursement, would supply forms and information for the insured to take to their physician to get a prescription, or might even make physicians available to write such prescriptions. And, of course, just like the large pharmaceutical firms, they could also make prescription-only versions of their vitamins or minerals.

In fact, there is probably little preventing an individual from creating such "prescription-only" packages themselves. Or from even creating their own WSA-type insurance policies by combining a trust agreement with a high-deductible insurance policy and a (self) restricted savings account.

One of the primary qualifications for an MSA account, and for most self-employed medical insurance tax deductions, is that the applicant not be currently eligible for medical insurance from their employer. This could limit many people with part-time self-employment income from getting the income tax advantages. However, as we will see in a moment, because most corporate policies no longer freely cover spouses and dependents, even individuals working for major corporations can now structure tax-advantaged wellness insurance policies for their families.

*   *   *

The 50 million self-employed individuals purchasing or structuring their own wellness insurance policies comprise the minority of the wellness insurance marketplace. The majority of the marketplace will come from the 187 million people currently covered by employer-based health insurance plans.

This majority will become wellness insurance consumers in two waves. The first wave will include the spouses and dependents of this group who voluntarily opt out of their breadwinners' corporate sickness insurance policy and structure their own wellness insurance policies. The second wave will be a forced restructuring of all employee-based sickness insurance plans that is currently being spearheaded by lawsuits in several states.

Employers used to pay the full health insurance premium for their employees *and* for their spouses and dependents. However most employers recently have changed to paying the full premium *only* for their employee. Spouses and dependents are now typically allowed to participate in the company group policy only if the additional premium is paid by the employee.

Since most employer-based policies are of the low- or zero-deductible type, switching a spouse or dependent to a wellness-oriented high-deductible policy will often save the employee money *while guaranteeing the spouse or dependent renewable affordable health insurance for life.* As previously explained, insurance companies may legally only raise premiums on individual policies equally for all individuals in a defined class rather than for specific persons who have filed large claims for medical care.

Keep in mind that not every spouse or dependent will medically qualify for such an individual policy— about 22 percent of them have some preexisting condition. But if your spouse or a dependent is in the fortunate 78-percent group, you should apply and price individual high-deductible medical insurance for them as soon as possible. In addition to saving you money, you never know when they might develop a condition that could limit their future eligibility, and thus your options for future employment.

If you utilize the services of an insurance agent to price such a policy, keep in mind that the commission on a low- or no-deductible policy is several times larger than the commission on a high-deductible one—even though the agent typically has to perform the same amount of work. One of the main reasons MSA accounts have not yet sold as well as expected is a reluctance by some insurance brokers to switch their customers to high-deductible policies that pay much lower commissions.[77]

It is estimated that spouses and dependents comprise about two-thirds, or 125 million, of the 187 million Americans with sickness insurance provided by an employer. Thus, approximately 97 million spouses and dependents (78 percent of this 125 million) could potentially save money switching to high-deductible policies and using some of their savings for wellness products and services. In cases where a breadwinner receives free sickness insurance for themselves from an employer, but also has some part-time income from a family business, shifting this income to the name of his or her spouse could allow the family to maximize the value of the new self-employment medical insurance tax deductions, as well as potentially qualify to open an MSA account.

Eventually, before most of these 97 million spouses and dependents make such a change, employers will be restructuring their health insurance offerings to allow employees to choose where to spend the employer health insurance contribution—and most employees will choose high-deductible wellness policies for themselves and their dependents. This restructuring, as noted earlier, is being forced upon employers by litigation, and it has

---

[77]In the aforementioned example, switching from the zero-deductible to the $2,500 deductible policy would lower the agent commission from $847 (17 percent of $4,980) to $324 (17 percent of $1,908). Agent commissions on health insurance policies are typically 17 percent of the first-year premium.

dire consequences for the 22 percent of employees who cannot obtain health insurance elsewhere because of a preexisting condition.

As medical costs and sickness insurance premiums have skyrocketed, employers have cut back on the number of medical services covered by their policies, services that include expensive diagnostics as well as early-intervention treatment. Lawsuits have succeeded in holding employers liable where an employee incurred greater injury by not getting such a diagnostic test or initial treatment. Ironically, employers, who once thought they'd be considered benevolent by paying for most medical expenses, are now being held liable for those medical expenses that they can no longer afford to pay.

The result of this litigation is that employers now want out of making the decisions on what is and is not covered by their corporate medical insurance.

The answer, as many employers have already discovered, is a "cafeteria" plan where the employer contributes a fixed and equal amount for medical insurance to each employee and gives the employee a list of options on how to spend it. Initially, all of their spending options will come from the same insurance company, because the insurer will only agree to cover the unfortunate 22 percent if the insurer gets the premium from the healthy 78 percent. But this will quickly break down as the healthy 78 percent begin demanding coverage for more and more wellness-type products and services rather than low-deductible sickness coverage.

As more employers institute such cafeteria plans, there will be less sickness benefits and services for the 22-percent group and more wellness services for the 78-percent group. Sadly, this could force many in the 22-percent group into financial hardship which in turn could force them to seek jobs with more favorable medical coverage, a positive development for employers who would prefer to have only employees in the "healthy" 78-percent group.

The cafeteria option plan is now sweeping through most major corporations. It is the beginning of the breakdown of the employer-group system—where the healthy 78 percent of employees pay for the unhealthy 22 percent. Congress will soon have no choice but to put politics aside and face the cold hard facts of reforming healthcare:

(1) Healthy Americans want more wellness options on a tax-deductible basis, and want economic credit for wellness decisions today that will save money tomorrow; and

(2) Private employers cannot be expected to pay (and pay and pay) for the unlimited sickness expenses of a minority of their employees—especially when this situation was created in part by government policies subsidizing sickness instead of wellness.

Congress actually began considering some of these issues in 1997 when it passed the legislation allowing the medical savings accounts "experiment." In addition to self-employed individuals, employees of small businesses (i.e., less than 50 employees) are allowed to set up company-sponsored MSAs where the employer makes tax-deductible contributions to each employee's individual MSA account. The employee is allowed to keep tax-free amounts not spent today to spend on future medical expenses tomorrow, even expenses occurring after the employee no longer works for the company.

This type of plan is exactly what employees in the 78-percent group will demand—especially once they learn that employees of other companies have already been granted this savings option through employer-sponsored MSAs. As noted earlier, individuals and corporations opening MSA accounts before January 31, 2002 are allowed to continue to make MSA contributions for the rest of their working lives.

*   *   *

Some readers, even those in the healthy 78 percent, may be getting upset by what may appear to be a callous attitude toward the unfortunate 22 percent. I ask for their indulgence; I am simply passing on the bad news, not advocating it. As painful as it may be to consider what is happening to a friend or a loved one in the 22-percent group, it is only by openly addressing this problem that we can hope to find a solution.

One of the best things about life in the United States today is Medicare—the federal health insurance program that pays most medical expenses for the 40 million U.S. citizens over age 65. Since it began in 1965, Medicare has bestowed enormous social benefits on seniors and their families. Prior to Medicare and Social Security, retirement often led to a severely reduced standard of living, if not outright poverty. But one of the worst things about life in the United States today is the absence of a federal healthcare program that pays most medical expenses for the 70 million U.S. citizens under age 18. The absence of such a program causes enormous social turmoil for children and their families.

Economically speaking, it is incredible that our society pays hundreds of billions for the medical costs of seniors, and pays virtually nothing for the medical costs of children (other than for the very poor).[78] Each time a senior incurs a medical expense,

---

[78]The very poor in the United States receive Medicaid—a $200 billion program that pays virtually all medical expenses for U.S.

his or her life is prolonged, and the government is assured of many more such expenses in the future.[79] Each time a child incurs a medical expense to cover costs of prevention as well as treatment of illness, in most cases their future economic productivity is improved, and our society receives back many times the cost of this medical investment.

This is especially true because one of the few areas of U.S. medicine that does a good job on disease prevention and wellness is pediatrics—dollars spent on inoculations and early disease detection in children routinely save hundreds of dollars in future medical costs, let alone earn society thousands of dollars by making children more productive taxpaying adults.

Hopefully, Congress will soon enact a Medicare-type program for all U.S. citizens under age 18. This will help ameliorate the problem for employees in the unfortunate 22-percent group with preexisting conditions in their families, and relieve employers of part of the burden of maintaining a social and economic safety net that has been unjustly thrust upon them.

The average U.S. household earns about $40,000 in after-tax annual income and spends (directly or indirectly through an employer) about one-seventh ($5,500) of this amount on medical expenses. This average figure belies the sad truth that tens of millions of U.S. households with annual incomes down to $20,000 or less spend the same $5,500 on medical costs. But, when family income falls below the poverty line (currently about $17,050 for a family of four[80]), virtually 100 percent of medical expenses

---

citizens under age 65 who live below the poverty line.

[79]It could be argued fairly that the seniors are the ones who built the great economy that now pays for their medical expenses.

[80]The U.S. Census bureau in 2000 defined $17,050 as the

are paid for by the government through the Medicaid insurance program.

Some families with chronically ill members are forced to stay deliberately unemployed just to qualify for Medicaid health insurance, just as some employees with preexisting medical conditions are forced to remain with their current employer. Meanwhile, seniors and hard-working families with incomes just above the poverty line often resent their "poorer" neighbors' health insurance benefits—particularly Medicaid's 100 percent coverage for prescription drugs. Even seniors on Medicare have to pay for prescription drugs, which is often the largest single monthly expense in the household of a retired couple. As previously noted, approximately 22 percent of prescriptions written today are not filled because of cost, and millions of people sadly make the terrible choice today between purchasing their food or their medicine. The solution here is not to cut Medicaid benefits, but to extend the same benefits, including prescription drug coverage, to seniors and middle-class Americans with family incomes below the $40,000 national average.

As the length of time spent with each employer continues to shrink, and as the unemployment time between jobs or careers continues to grow, more families will experience periods without health insurance. As employers become more sophisticated at screening out new hires with preexisting medical conditions in their families, more otherwise productive individuals will remain unemployed—and uninsured. And as our population naturally ages,

---

"poverty line" for a family of four in the 48 states (as well as $21,320 in Alaska and $19,610 in Hawaii), plus or minus $2,900 for each additional or subtracted family member. ("The 2000 HHS Poverty Guidelines," U.S. Department of Health and Human Services)

more employees will develop preexisting conditions that limit their ability to change jobs—jobs that would pay them more and better utilize their services, to the benefit of all.

These and other workplace inefficiencies caused by employer-provided sickness insurance are disrupting the U.S. labor supply, which ultimately generates the $10 trillion economy that pays for our $1.4 trillion in medical expenses.

Eventually, the federal government will have to enact some type of basic sickness, hospitalization, and prescription drug insurance for all Americans unrelated to their employment—first for seniors, then for children, and then for everyone else. If properly enacted, such a national sickness insurance program would actually save U.S. taxpayers money and provide a boom to the emerging wellness industry.

Here's how a such an eventual solution would work.

Keep in mind first that the government cannot universally pay *all* medical expenses. Medical costs are unlimited if left unchecked. Almost every prematurely born infant or terminally ill patient could be kept alive by technology—especially if no regard is given to the quality of that continued life. And even healthy people could consume unlimited amounts of emerging new treatments, from Viagra for sexual impotence to Rogaine for thinning hair. As medical technology continues to expand its offering of products and services, medical expenses could easily double from one-seventh to two-sevenths of our gross domestic product.

Instead, a national sickness insurance program would cover only predefined sickness industry costs for citizens over age 18—products and services provided reactively to people with existing diseases. It would have a fixed amount that would be payable for each treatment or operation, just as Medicare and many private insurance programs have today for their covered procedures at "usual and customary" levels of payment to healthcare providers.

This basic program would also have limits for certain procedures determined by the age of the patient—such as not covering heart surgery for persons over 80 years old. Conversely, for citizens under age 18, the basic program should cover most wellness products and services from inoculations to nutritional supplements. This would pay for itself by improving the opportunity for each child to actualize his or her maximum economic earning (and tax-paying) potential.

Such universal basic sickness coverage would actually be economically neutral to the total U.S. economy. Uninsured Americans already are receiving such basic sickness benefits today—although many have to go on welfare or travel to overloaded and inefficient hospital emergency rooms to get them. For most working Americans, this program would represent a transfer in sickness insurance responsibility from employers to government, the costs of which could be phased in over time. On the provider side, it would represent a shift from public hospitals and charities to more efficient private and public providers—universal sickness coverage would spawn the entry of highly efficient providers into the market. Companies like Wal-Mart and McDonald's would efficiently offer specialized sickness industry procedures at convenient locations.

But the real benefit for most Americans would be the supplemental premium sickness and wellness insurance programs that would emerge from the private sector.

Most working Americans would not be satisfied with a basic capitated government sickness insurance program that limited the amount spent on each treatment or within a given time period. They, or their employers, would purchase supplemental insurance to cover a premium level of sickness industry services—from private rooms at hospitals to better providers to more diagnostic tests. And, such premium supplemental insurance programs would also include tax-deductible MSA-type savings components for wellness industry products and services.

In addition to covering a higher level of sickness services, premium supplement programs such as MSAs would allow consumers many options in wellness decision-making—since consumers would be spending their own money on wellness products and services. A typical $5,000 tax-deductible annual premium might contain a $1,000 component for supplemental sickness insurance and $4,000 to be spent or saved for wellness industry products and services.

This would lead to a restructuring of the health insurance industry away from the adversarial relationship that exists today between the insured and their insurers. Once relieved of providing catastrophic sickness coverage for past events and covering prior existing conditions, insurance companies could focus their energies proactively on wellness—since as supplemental sickness insurers they would also share the benefits of efficacious wellness decisions. Just as accident insurers routinely inspect their insured's plants and make suggestions on how to increase safety, wellness insurance companies could take active roles in keeping their policyholders aware of the latest developments in wellness technology and services.

Most employers today would relish the opportunity to increase wages and opt out of providing any health insurance benefits for their employees. When the government gets around to providing basic sickness coverage for all, this could provide employers the opportunity to get out of health insurance and focus fully on what they do best: running their own business.

Chapter 8

Epilogue

Economically, we measure our food and medical crisis in dollars and population.

We spend $1.4 trillion in the United States each year on sickness, about one-seventh of every dollar we earn. Approximately 77 million Americans—27 percent of our population—are clinically obese. And 184 million Americans—61 percent—are overweight and unhealthy.

These numbers have doubled over the last few decades and risen 10 percent in just the last five years. Moreover, this epidemic is already rampant in most other developed nations.

Yet even these enormous numbers far belie the true cost of our dilemma. For the true cost in human suffering cannot be measured in trillions of dollars, or in millions of people.

Each of the 77 million people who are obese represents a life misspent. These individuals don't have the energy to fully enjoy their lives, their work and their families. They spend a significant portion of their lives on a medical merry-go-round that treats a minimal amount of their symptoms—just enough to keep them alive and consuming more unhealthy food and more sickness products and services. And their lives are cut tragically short—obesity is ultimately the primary contributing cause of most nongeriatric deaths.

Even worse, the obese in our population are widely discriminated against and unjustly accused of entirely creating the problem.

The 107 million overweight, but not obese, individuals in the United States are not that much better off. Even if they have learned to live with their extra pounds, they are often malnourished to the point of fatigue, nervousness, headaches, confusion and muscle weakness. And when they turn to their medical community for help, they are told that these issues are normal symptoms of advancing age, rather than problems caused by the same poor diet of "empty calories" that causes their extra pounds.

Furthermore, at every turn, powerful economic forces ally themselves to turn these overweight individuals into their obese cousins.

Five years ago, when I began the research that led me to write this book, I was not optimistic that a solution could be found. Although in my lifetime I had seen the virtual demise of communism and significant improvements in combating world hunger and racial discrimination, I felt we could not overcome our entrapment in the "sickness" approach to healthcare. The reason I was pessimistic is that ultimately these problems are caused by economic issues. I remembered the famous quotation from John Maynard Keynes, who wrote:

> "The ideas of economists . . . are more powerful than is commonly understood. Indeed, the world is ruled by little else. Practical men, who believe themselves to be quite exempt from any intellectual influences, are usually the slaves of some defunct economist."[81]

These unfortunate individuals, now totaling 61 percent of the U.S. population, have become slaves to the combined economic interests of the $1 trillion food industry and the $1.4 trillion sickness industry.

---

[81]John Maynard Keynes, *The General Theory of Employment, Interest, and Money*, (San Diego: Harcourt Brace Jovanovich, 1964), 383. Keynes' great work was first published in England in 1936.

But as my research progressed I began to see an economic solution to this economic problem.

The companies and individuals in the emerging wellness industry seek personal economic gain when they go out each day to market their wares. But in doing so, they carry a message that is far more important than the actual products or services they are trying to sell. Underlying the pitch for each product is the message that you, individually, can do something about the obesity and ill health that afflicts the majority of our citizens.

In marketing a new product, it typically takes three affirmative decisions on the part of a consumer before he or she actually tries the product. And it takes even more exposures to the product and its benefits to get to each affirmative decision. Each time a wellness message reaches a consumer, even when the consumer does not favorably respond, the message brings the consumer one step closer to making an affirmative decision that may change his or her entire life.

And once consumers try a product and have a positive wellness product experience, they typically become voracious consumers of more wellness products and services.

- The single mother who lost 35 pounds now wants to join a fitness club for even more energy.

- The boy with more energy from a new vitamin regimen now wants to learn about better nutrition and change his diet.

- The father who eliminated pain with magnetic therapy now wants to learn about better vitamins.

- The parents of a girl without colds thanks to echinacea now want to learn what's available for their other children.

- The former athlete using glucosamine who has returned to bicycling now wants something to improve his memory.

- And the prostate patient who was cured with saw palmetto now wants to spread his message about naturopathic experiences.

As explained in Chapter Four, each satisfied wellness customer is just beginning a lifetime of consumption of products and services that have the potential to improve every aspect of life at every moment.

In 1776, Adam Smith's *The Wealth of Nations* described how the unfettered pursuit by individuals of their own selfish interests leads directly to the increased well-being of the total society. The deeper and deeper Smith delved into the workings of the economy, the more fascinated he became by what he called "the invisible hand" that guided the actions of individuals toward increased societal wealth. And although Smith, as a progressive scientist in a secular and enlightened era, avoided using *His* or *Her* name, it is clear upon reading the original work that Adam Smith knew whose *Invisible Hand* was at work.

Today, there is no better example of God's hand at work than in the emerging wellness industry and the positive economic forces behind the revolution that is about to take place.

*   *   *

So the LORD blessed the latter end of Job more than his beginning: for he had fourteen thousand sheep, and six thousand camels, and a thousand yoke

of oxen, and a thousand she asses. He had also seven sons and three daughters.....And in all the land were no women found so fair as the daughters of Job: and their father gave them inheritance among their brethren. After this lived Job a hundred and forty years, and saw his sons, and his sons' sons, even four generations. So Job died, being old and full of days.
Job 42:12-17 (King James Bible)

My father was a religious man. He firmly believed in a true and just God who had a reason for everything. Even while he was dying of cancer, he never wavered in his belief that his own medical situation and society's economic problems were both the result of our failure to utilize the tools that God has given us. He firmly believed, quoting Albert Einstein, that God does not play dice with the universe.

I took this belief with me to Wharton Graduate Business School almost thirty years ago. It was there that I began to see the wonderful underlying order in the free-market economy—an order that could only have been built by a just and loving God who wanted all of His children to have the opportunity to prosper.

When students first study the physical sciences, they often find God absent from their initial discoveries. Science seems so exact in explaining the mysteries of the galaxy through deductive logic that religious doctrine based on faith seems superfluous. It is only when they develop a much higher knowledge in a chosen field—when the basic rules that once seemed so complex become so glaringly obvious—that students realize only a Supreme Being could have created a universe of such magnificent order and laid it open for us to discover how it works. Many of our great scientists, like Albert Einstein, started out as atheists but became deeply spiritual in later life.

Although my father cherished Einstein's quotation that God does not play dice with the universe, Einstein actually made a great mistake when he said it. This mistake as a young man led to "a fruitless quest that occupied the rest of his life."[82,83]

Einstein was searching for what came to be known as a unified field theory, a theory which would explain the behavior of everything in the universe from the smallest electron to the largest planet. But in doing so, Einstein could not accept that individual atomic particles appeared to move at random, like dice, but that when millions of particles were observed as a whole their actions followed established laws of probability.

Today, the science of quantum mechanics, which is based on this probabilistic behavior of elementary particles, gives us everything from nuclear energy to personal computers. What Einstein failed to take into account, is that God invented dice and that God also gave us the science of statistics to understand how dice work.[84]

---

[82]Albert Einstein, *Encyclopaedia Britannica,* 2000. Although Einstein's discoveries as a physicist may have been fruitless from this point forward, Einstein certainly more than distinguished himself in his later years as a statesman and champion of world peace.

[83]Einstein was professionally ostracized by other leading physicists because of his refusal to accept the probabilistic laws of quantum mechanics—although they later successfully used his fame and political connections during World War II. Einstein was called upon by them to get President Roosevelt to endorse the Manhattan Project to build the atomic bomb, but then Einstein was kept in the dark about their progress until the bomb was actually detonated over Hiroshima.

[84]My friend and colleague Norman Beil disagrees with me that Einstein was incorrect on this point. Beil contends that statistics are used to make decisions only when we do not have the right

This mathematical concept of frequency, that individual events don't always follow established rules but that many events do over time, is one of the hardest things for my students, and beginning entrepreneurs, to understand.

Here's an experiment I performed for twenty years on the first day of class at New York University:

I asked my students to flip a coin ten times and to record the result. To their astonishment, many wound up with heads (or tails) appearing 80 to 90 percent of the time versus the expected 50 percent. Then I asked them to do the same exercise one hundred times—when they did this they individually almost always recorded heads or tails appearing 47 to 53 percent of the time.

This, I would explain, is why they should not allow published statistics to influence their individual decision-making in areas in which they will never encounter enough frequency, like getting married or deciding upon a career. In areas like these, in which they will make decisions only a few times over the course of their lives, they will never have enough frequency for established statistics to be a relevant indicator of their success. What matters most, of course, are things like *who* they decide to marry or *how much* they are committed to a particular endeavor.

But, I would further explain, statistical data can be extremely useful when we are careful enough to apply such data only to situations where we will encounter enough frequency from which to derive

---

answer—as in meteorology, where we use statistical data to predict a "28 percent chance of rain" even though whether or not it will rain is a binary outcome. Beil feels that Einstein was saying we should not give up searching for a unified field theory and rely on statistics, but rather that we should keep searching for the correct answer in this important quest.

probable outcomes.

In the businesses I've been involved in over the years, I've never been concerned with the success of a particular event or transaction. Instead, I've tried to follow a steady course of action on many similar transactions (say, a sales call with a specific pitch), and then retrospectively analyze the results only when I've had enough frequency to make a worthwhile analysis.

As a manager, a teacher and a part-time clergy person, I have been continually asked by young people "how come" such and such an effort didn't lead to the expected reward. While I've tried to console them, I, too, have been frustrated that although God made a world with rules and order, God also made a world in which those rules are not absolute. Some people think God did this because God didn't want people to become too cocky by having things work out for them every time. Or some people think God wanted to give a chance to those who weren't born with what society then dictated they needed to succeed.

I think that the reason God did this was to create a world that would constantly challenge, and thus strengthen, our faith. A world where everything doesn't work out *each* time, but a world where everything does work out *over* time—especially for those of us, like Job, with enough faith to follow God's laws regardless of how much adversity we experience.

But in some situations, particularly in economics, sometimes it seems as if almost nothing is working out over time. This has occurred when, however well-intentioned, we have created economic or legal anomalies hampering the free market from reaching its natural objective. Or sometimes such anomalies can occur when we fail to affirmatively take action to correct unfair situations.

For example, the laws and obligations for individuals to own and use real property productively are spelled out in the first book of the Bible.[85] In the first half of the twentieth century, countries making up almost half of the world adopted a new system of shared property ownership, or communism, which they thought would lead to increased prosperity for all. This legislated anomaly, called communism, caused their economies to collapse literally to the point of starvation. But by the end of the twentieth century, the anomaly fixed itself as most of this half of the world voluntarily abandoned communism in favor of free markets, capitalism and free enterprise.

In the United States near the end of the nineteenth century, certain wealthy individuals found a way to artificially limit competition and equal economic opportunity. Working through trusts to hide their activities, these individuals created monopolies and cartels that lowered prices below cost to drive competition out of business deliberately— and then raised prices once they controlled all the providers in a marketplace. Beginning in 1890, Congress passed a series of antitrust laws limiting the ability to stifle competition and exploit others when economic power becomes too concentrated.[86]

In our time, these antitrust laws were used in

---

[85]In Genesis 23:17, Abraham becomes the first person in the Bible to recognize land as individual property that can be improved, purchased and sold. Abraham purchases for 400 shekels of silver the field of Ephron together with the trees on the land and the Cave of Machpelah as a burying place for his wife, Sarah. The discussion over the price, the exacting legal description of the property, and the public announcement of the acquisition before those who entered the city (Hebron) contain the basic elements of all present-day contracts for the sale of real property.

[86]The Sherman Antitrust Act of 1890 declared any agreement to fix prices, limit output, or exclude competition to be illegal.

1984 to break up the monopoly on long distance calls held by AT&T. This led directly to a fivefold reduction in long distance charges, great innovations and improved services, and a vastly improved economy for all, including AT&T, which today is worth many times what it was in 1984. Some of us can remember when we couldn't profitably do business or keep in contact with people who were a "long distance" call away.

In 1982, I could see the savings and loan crisis coming when Congress passed a law "deregulating" the S&L industry—allowing these financial institutions to put their deposits in high-yield risky investments.[87] Congress thought it was deregulating these institutions by letting them compete for consumers' deposits, who were then demanding higher and higher interest rates. But unfortunately, Congress created a great economic anomaly because the U.S. government was still "regulating" S&Ls by guaranteeing the principal and interest on the deposits. Unscrupulous operators were then able to take over these institutions and loot more than $200 billion in public funds before Congress stopped their activities in 1989.

The greatest economic anomalies today exist in our food and healthcare industries.

The trillion-dollar food industry has found a profitable model for itself that targets already-obese consumers for ever-increasing consumption. This continues because of an economic anomaly where

---

[87] I originally told my story to then-Vice President George Bush in 1983, which led to me testifying before Congress in 1984 at hearings on the Bush Task Force on Financial Reform. Later, after spending years in the media exposing different parts of the crisis, I wrote (with Robert Deitz) *Other People's Money* (Simon & Schuster, 1989) which told the story of the debacle that cost U.S. taxpayers more than $200 billion.

third parties—the government (through Medicare and Medicaid) and employers (through private health insurance)—pick up the medical cost of their activities.

A similar economic anomaly used to exist in the case of environmental pollution, until the government began taxing industrial corporations for damaging the environment and made them pay for the costs of repairing that damage. But in the case of attempts by certain state legislatures to tax junk food, it currently seems unlikely that government will pursue a similar avenue of attack on the damage done to public health and welfare by the food industry.[88]

The trillion-dollar sickness industry finds it more profitable to focus on the symptoms versus the cures of disease, creating customers for life. This continues because of an economic anomaly where someone other than patients and their physicians are making the key decisions about their health. Our employer-funded healthcare system has led the medical industry far from the needs of their ultimate consumer—a consumer who would much prefer a cure versus an ongoing addiction to a treatment.

These and other economic anomalies will eventually be corrected. But, meanwhile, their existence has created the greatest opportunity of this millennium: the opportunity to make a financial fortune by providing the ultimate fortune of wellness to an entire population. For there are no riches that surpass having a healthy body.

---

[88]In 1990 the legislatures of California, Maryland, and Maine considered bills taxing junk food such as candy bars and potato chips. These efforts were met with heavy opposition from the Snack Food Association and were eventually defeated.

Appendix 1

Food—An Economic Perspective

And unto Adam he said, Because thou hast...eaten of the tree.....cursed is the ground for thy sake; in sorrow (toil) shalt thou eat of it all the days of thy life..... In the sweat of thy face shalt thou eat bread.....Therefore the LORD God sent him forth from the garden of Eden, to till the ground from whence he was taken.

Genesis, Chapter 1 (King James Bible)

Adam and Eve didn't worry too much about food. According to the Bible, the Garden of Eden freely contained "every tree that is pleasant to the sight, and good for food."[89] Then, because Eve tasted the apple, the ground was cursed so that it would only yield food with hard labor.

Ever since then, the search for food has dominated our existence. But what is food, and why it is so necessary for human existence?

In addition to enjoying food because it tastes good, human beings require food for three purposes:

(1) **Energy:** fuel (calories) necessary to perform external work and to simply allow the heart, lungs and other organs to function;

(2) **Building blocks:** raw materials (e.g., proteins, most minerals) used to manufacture blood, skin, bones, hair and internal organs; the

---

[89]Genesis 2:9 (King James Bible)

human body is constantly replacing and renewing every cell on a daily to monthly basis;[90] and

(3) **Catalysts:** Chemical compounds (e.g., vitamins, enzymes and some minerals) necessary to facilitate the chemical reactions that convert food into energy and into bodily organs.

Human beings require food for energy every few hours and require specific foods for building blocks and catalysts on a daily or semi-daily basis. Our bodies are biologically programmed to immediately sense when energy is needed—we experience hunger pain. Unfortunately, we usually become aware of missing building blocks or catalysts only when our bodies become ill from these deficiencies.

Our bodies are also biologically programmed to seek out foods containing the highest amounts of energy—foods containing the highest amounts of energy (e.g., sugar, fat) taste the best.

This biological programming, and its successful exploitation by the commercial providers of our food supply, is the major cause of poor health in the developed world today.

The United States is the poorest of the developed nations when it comes to health—U.S. citizens are the most obese and spend more than three times as much money on medical care than their European or Asian counterparts. This massive difference, not just in the cost of medical care but also in the unhappiness caused by poor health, is the result of

---

[90]Our bodies manufacture 200 billion red blood cells each day, replacing all the blood in our body every 120 days. Skin is completely replaced every 1 to 3 months. It takes 90 days for old bone to be broken down and replaced by new bone.

our having a terrible diet.

There are two major problems with the diet of most people in the United States.

First, we eat too much—fully 61 percent of our citizens are overweight.

Second, most of us are not getting the minimum amounts of building blocks and/or catalysts that our bodies need.

In order to understand and cure these problems, it is first necessary to summarize briefly how our bodies process food into energy and living matter.

All food substances are made of one or more of the following six nutrient categories:

Water
Carbohydrates: sugars, breads, etc.
Lipids: fats, oils, etc.
Proteins: meat, fish, eggs, vegetables, etc.
Vitamins: fruits, vegetables, etc.
Minerals: fruits, vegetables, etc.

Digestion begins when food enters your mouth and starts being broken down by your teeth and the enzymes in your saliva. Then chemicals in your stomach go to work digesting the food into its six nutrient categories.

The human body is composed of about 60 percent water and requires a minimum of two quarts of fresh water per day. *If possible, you should try to avoid drinking this water during mealtimes. The chemicals in your stomach become less efficacious when diluted, and this can cause valuable nutrients to wash through versus being absorbed by your body.*

The energy contained in a specific portion of food, and the energy needs of the body, are both measured in units called calories. The number of calories in a particular food can be measured by burning a weighed portion of the food and measuring the amount of heat that is produced. It is also possible to measure the number of calories burned by a particular physical activity, ranging from just sleeping to jogging up a steep hill.

Of the six nutrient categories, only carbohydrates (4 calories per gram), lipids or fats (9 calories per gram), and proteins (4 calories per gram) provide energy.[91]

The human body requires approximately 2,200 calories of energy per day for a woman and 2,900 calories per day for a man. A person doing daily athletic exercise requires more calories per day than a sedentary person. Figure 1.1 shows the amount of calories burned per half hour by different types of activities. At any level of activity, the human body uses about 65 percent of its energy for basal metabolic functions like breathing and pumping blood.

Figure 1.1: Calories Burned per 30 Minutes of Activity[92]

Activity (30 minutes)	120 lb. Person	175 lb. Person
Bicycling 14-16 mph	288	420
Skiing – downhill	238	346
Bicycling – Mountain	230	336
Jogging	191	278
Swimming – moderate	166	242
Tennis – singles	166	242
Golf – carry clubs	166	242
Walking 4 mph	140	205
Weight lifting – general	94	136
Golf – with cart	94	136
Sitting	29	42
Sleeping	25	37

---

[91]Proteins are typically not digested into energy because they are the most difficult to digest and because the body needs these building blocks to constantly replace its organs.

[92]Data compiled from Healthstatus.com (http://www.health-status.com).

When a person's daily intake of calories exceeds their daily bodily requirements, the body converts these excess calories into fat, which is then stored throughout the body. A normal amount of fat, typically between 15 and 25 percent of body mass, is important for hundreds of bodily functions. These functions range from maintaining temperature to absorbing fat-soluble vitamins to cushioning vital organs. If a person has too little fat in their system, the body will begin destructively breaking down their muscles and internal organs to meet its requirements for energy.

However, when a person consumes more calories than the body uses over a period of time, their body starts to store excess fat in visible places. This excess fat often first appears in the stomach on a man and on the thighs in a woman. Excess fat is associated with fatigue, heart disease, cancer and hundreds of other life-threatening diseases. (See Appendix 2: Fat—What Is It, and How Much Is Too Much?)

Theoretically, before it becomes life threatening, this excess stored fat should be converted back into calories when the body next requires more energy. Unfortunately, this does not typically occur today for four main reasons:

(1) We consume available carbohydrate calories before fat calories;

(2) Our bodies tell us to look for more food before using stored reserves;

(3) Readily-available food causes our metabolism to stabilize at the higher fat level; and

(4) The type of food we eat today is different than it was when our biological formula for energy storage was developed.

First, just as a hungry person consumes the most readily available source of food, the human body always consumes the most easily convertible source of energy. Of the nutrients containing calories, molecules of carbohydrates are the simplest in form and thus are the easiest for the body to quickly convert into energy. This is why people crave carbohydrates when they haven't eaten for a while or immediately after performing strenuous exercise.

In contrast, molecules of fat are more complex and require additional energy and additional time to be converted (or burned) back into energy. The body always looks to available carbohydrates first for energy before it begins to break down ingested and then stored molecules of fat.

Second, when a person needs energy he or she experiences hunger (typically for more carbohydrates) long before their body turns to its stores of excess fat. This biological programming served us well in prehistoric times—telling prehistoric man to keep eating (and eating and eating) when food was plentiful before drawing on his stored reserves. We are biologically programmed to eat each meal as if it could be the last one we were going to get for a long time—and in many cases it was before humankind learned how to preserve foods, to farm, and to domesticate animals.

The ability to make conscious choices contrary to our biological programming is what separates us from most of the animal kingdom. Humans and animals have virtually the same biologically-driven appetites or desires which yield pleasure when satisfied, with one all-important difference: Humans have a mind and soul that is superior to and can control their biological desires. Unfortunately, this seems true for most people today in every area except their dining habits.

Some animals have learned how to supersede their biological programming in our world of abundant food. Many people with pets today use dried food and leave it out to be consumed on a leisurely basis, rather than waiting until their pet begs for its next meal. Veterinarians and pet owners have learned that if you only feed your pet when it gets very hungry, they will eat the full amount given to them even if their bodies no longer require it. However, if food is continuously available, most pets will adjust their appetites and eat only what they need for optimum health. Sadly, this is a lesson that most doctors and U.S. citizens have yet to learn for themselves and their own children.

We also eat much faster today than our parents did—when everyone had to sit for long time periods around the table and share conversation. It typically takes 10-15 minutes from the time we ingest food until our hunger becomes sated—this is why you are sometimes no longer hungry at a restaurant when an entrée arrives late. *When we take time between courses or bites to digest our food, our hunger becomes satisfied with just the amount of calories we require. But when we eat quickly at our desk between appointments or at fast-food restaurants, we often think we are hungry and keep eating even though we have already ingested more than enough calories.*

Third, when a person puts on additional fat, say 15 pounds of weight during a vacation with lavish meals, their daily basal metabolic requirement for calories increases. Where this person's hunger used to be sated with 2,500 calories per day, they now require approximately 3,000 calories in order not to feel hungry—their body and appetite having reached a new equilibrium at the heavier, 15-pound level. As long as food is readily available and people listen to their stomachs (hunger) regarding how much to eat, their increased amount of weight will remain. Once a person puts on excess weight he or she will most likely have to take proactive measures (e.g., diet) to lose it.

And fourth, the final and main reason that this stored excess fat may not be converted back into calories is because our food today is very different than food was when our biological program for storing energy was developed—it contains much more fat. When our biological programming for food was developed, our ancestors ate mostly a low-fat vegetarian diet with some game meats. And those foods containing fat had much less fat than they do today—game meats contain about 5 percent fat by weight versus the 30 percent fat by weight contained today in commercially-produced and hormonally-treated domesticated animals.

Back then, fat was so rare and so useful that our taste buds evolved to crave it and the parts of the animals that contained most of it. Today, unfortunately, this sensory craving has been exploited by our food suppliers: Like the first victim in the movie *Seven* about the monastic seven deadly sins, we are literally eating ourselves to death.

In just the last century we have almost doubled the percent of fat in our diets—from getting 20 percent of our calories from fat in 1910 to about 35 percent today.[93] But, this 35 percent average number belies the fact that our nation is divided when it comes to health: Millions of upscale Americans eat diets getting 20 percent or less of their calories from fat, and millions more eat diets getting 50 percent or more of their calories from life-threatening fat. Most experts agree that our bodies are biologically programmed for a diet requiring about 20 percent of our calories from fat.

The second major problem with the diet of most U.S. citizens is that they are not getting the minimum

---

[93]"Forward into the Past: Eating as Our Ancestors Did," Eating for Health, http://www.obesity.com

amounts of building blocks and/or catalysts that their bodies require.

While most adults think of their bodies as fully grown, the individual cells that comprise their organs actually replace themselves on a daily to monthly schedule. These cells contain over 100,000 different proteins comprised of 20 different amino acids. Food supplies us with plant and animal proteins containing the amino acids that our bodies require as the building blocks of our living tissue. *Without this daily supply, no matter how much energy we get in the form of calories, our bodies and minds deteriorate because we are not able to replace the dying cells in our internal and external organs.*

Food also supplies us certain minerals we require as building blocks to repair and regenerate our living matter. There are 14 essential minerals, some of which are required as catalysts rather than as building blocks. Seven of these are *major minerals,* defined as those of which we need more than 100 milligrams per day calcium, chloride, magnesium, phosphorus, potassium, sodium and sulfur. The remaining seven are called *trace minerals,* such as iron and zinc.

In addition to supplying proteins and minerals as building blocks, food contains the 13 essential vitamins our bodies require as catalysts to convert food into energy and to convert amino acids into bodily tissue. A catalyst is a substance that must be present, typically in a very small quantity, for a specific chemical reaction to occur.[94] For example,

---

[94]The chemical composition of a catalyst is not altered by the reaction, and thus a single catalyst molecule can be used over and over again. This explains why we only need such a small quantity of each vitamin—although we do need to ingest these small quantities daily, because most vitamins do not remain in the digestive system.

without Vitamin B3, which is contained in green leafy vegetables and unprocessed grains, our bodies cannot break down plant and animal proteins into basic amino acids. It doesn't matter how much protein you eat if your body can't convert it into the building blocks of your living tissue.

When we don't get enough protein, vitamins and minerals, our initial symptoms include mood swings, fatigue, nervousness, headaches, confusion and muscle weakness. Over the longer term, such poor nutrition can cause cancer, hypertension, Alzheimer's disease and many other diseases that we used to just accept as part of our aging process. *Modern medicine typically treats these problems with drugs that focus on each symptom rather than on the underlying problem, which is what we eat, or more correctly in the case of poor nutrition, what we don't eat.*

But before you become too alarmed that you're never going to get enough of all these critical nutrients, here is some good news. Our bodies only require a small amount of protein and a minuscule amount of minerals and vitamins on a daily basis.

The human body requires approximately 46 grams (1.6 ounces) of protein per day for women and 58 grams (2.0 ounces) of protein per day for men. This is less than most people believe they need thanks to successful but misleading advertising campaigns by the beef and cattle industry. Ironically, meat and milk products are actually a poor source of protein because they contain high amounts of harmful fats when compared to other protein sources such as fish, nuts, breads and vegetables.

The human body requires 13 essential vitamins in dosages ranging from 60 milligrams per day for vitamin C to 200 micrograms per day for vitamin B8 (folic acid). These quantities are naturally abundant in commonly available fresh foods.

Similarly, even the 14 minerals we require are

also contained in fresh foods in more than adequate quantities—100 milligrams is only 3/1000 of an ounce.

Now here's the bad news: Despite the relatively small amounts of proteins, vitamins and minerals we require on a daily basis, and their abundance in natural foods, our biologically programmed need for these substances is not being met by our modern food supply.

When our ancestors were hunter-gatherers they subsisted on a plant-rich diet of nuts, fruits, beans, grains and roots, with some game meats. Because no single type of food was in abundance, while they searched primarily for calories they automatically consumed the variety of foods containing the different proteins, vitamins and minerals that their bodies required. (Or, conversely, their bodies adapted to the nutrients in the variety of foods they consumed.)

Over time, these hunter-gatherers became farmers. Using human ingenuity and the economic abundance that results from specialization, they learned how to efficiently produce large quantities of specific foods that they could then trade for other foods. More significantly, they learned how to produce the foods that naturally tasted the best and could last the longest—-foods rich in fat like dried meats and aged cheeses. World population rose steadily from around 200 million at the time of Jesus Christ to about 1 billion by the end of the nineteenth century.

In the twentieth century, rising agricultural technology finally eliminated the age-old problem of not having enough food—with a vengeance. Thanks to the "green revolution," India and China went from starvation economies to becoming net exporters of food. World population rose from 1 billion to 6 billion. Thanks to agrarian technology, which was led by the United States, between 1930 and 1980 the United

States went from 30 million farmers barely producing enough food for a domestic population of 100 million people, to 3 million farmers producing more than enough food for 300 million people. Farm production became more and more efficient, with no end in sight.

The United States Department of Agriculture (USDA) was originally created to safeguard the economic interests of farmers, particularly in times of drought and famine. During this period of rising agricultural efficiency, the USDA budget was shifted to government "farm income stabilization" programs that paid farmers billions each year not to grow more food, in order to keep food prices higher and thus safeguard the farmers' economic interests. Today, in addition to forcing consumers to pay higher prices for food, these subsidies keep many farmers from learning how to use new technology and from changing to grow crops that consumers really want. Worst of all, this subsidy—$18.405 billion in 1999 alone—encourages many young people to become farmers even though our economy no longer needs more farmers.[95]

Yet despite efforts to the contrary by the USDA, the relative price for farm produce fell steadily throughout the second half of the twentieth century as supply far exceeded demand.

As the price farmers received for basic food fell, the profit opportunity in agriculture shifted from producing raw foodstuffs (e.g., wheat, milk, fruit, cattle) to manufacturing these foodstuffs into name-brand foods with long shelf lives (e.g., cereals, condiments, processed cheeses, canned foods, frozen foods and junk or snack foods). It became particularly profitable to make junk or snack foods, products that initially consumers didn't know they

---

[95]"No. 549, Federal Outlay by Detailed Function: 1990 to 1999," *Statistical Abstract of the United States: 1999.*

wanted but for which they had a seemingly unlimited propensity to consume.

Additionally, in the postwar U.S. economy the supply and demand for a new type of food arose—a food type not defined by its taste, price or availability, but defined by its speed of service: fast food.

During this period of great technological advances in our food supply, our knowledge of basic nutrition was just evolving. Many of our food scientists and engineers, let alone the consuming public, didn't know enough about the need for proteins, vitamins and minerals. Each food company concentrated on making each product taste better than that of the competition, last longer, and be safe from contamination by microorganisms.

Looking back, they did an admirable job at fulfilling their mission. Processed and fast food effectively didn't exist for most Americans at the end of World War II. By the end of the twentieth century, processed and fast-food sales had risen to about one-seventh of the U.S. gross domestic product, about $1 trillion per year.

But, despite making basic calories affordable for everyone, our food industry unwittingly injured the health of much of the nation.

In order to make their products taste better, they added fat. The better it tasted, the more customers ate of their products. The more customers ate of their products, the fatter they became. The fatter customers became, the more food products they were able to consume on a daily basis. And so on, and so on, and so on.

In order to make their products safe from contamination, they pasteurized and/or heated them.[96] Today all canned foods and virtually all milk

---

[96]Pasteurization is the application of heat to "destroy pathogenic (disease-producing) microorganisms, to inactivate spoilage-

and juices are pasteurized. Unfortunately, the application of heat to food, as well as its storage over time in cans and other airtight containers, destroys many of the vitamins and minerals. In general, canning and most other types of food processing do not affect proteins, fats and carbohydrates.

And in order to increase the shelf life of their products (as well as add to their safety), food producers added preservatives ranging from enormous amounts of sodium to a dizzying array of chemical compounds in supposedly "safe" amounts. While a typical adult requires about 500 milligrams a day of sodium which is found naturally in common foods, salt is so widely added to most processed foods that the typical U.S. adult consumes ten to fourteen times this amount per day. In addition to desensitizing our taste buds so that natural unprocessed foods no longer taste good, salt is the primary cause of high blood pressure which leads to increased risk of stroke, heart disease and kidney failure.

The end result is that today the U.S. food supply is dominated by what nutritional experts call "empty calories"—food containing high amounts of caloric energy but low (or empty) in essential vitamins, minerals and proteins.

Our bodies can only consume 2,200 to 2,900 calories per day for energy without becoming obese, but must get the required amounts of protein, vitamins, minerals and healthy fats along with these calories. Just a quick glance at the nutritional facts printed on any processed food label shows us what we are not getting along with our calories.

---

causing enzymes, and to reduce or destroy spoilage microorganisms" ("Food Preservation," *Encyclopaedia Britannica*, 2000).

A typical can of soda contains 140 empty calories (38 milligrams of sugar, 70 milligrams of sodium, added caffeine, various preservatives and 0 milligrams of proteins, vitamins and minerals). A typical fast-food meal contains an incredible 1,000 calories or more with almost no vitamins or minerals. One 1 ounce serving of Lay's Potato Chips ("You can't eat just one") contains 230 empty calories (plus 270 mg of sodium).

But these foods are much worse for what they do contain than for what they are missing: Most "empty calorie" foods have incredibly high levels of fat, which is added to make them taste better. A healthy food should yield about 20 percent of its calories from fat (each gram of fat contains 9 calories) and the rest from carbohydrates and proteins. Just one deluxe McDonald's burger contains 810 calories with an incredible 490 calories (55 grams, or 61 percent) from fat. Even without the medium-size french fries (containing 450 additional calories, with 22 grams additional fat), *55 grams of fat is the full amount you should consume in an entire day, not the amount you should consume from a single item of food.*[97]

In contrast, foods in their natural (unprocessed) state are packed with caloric energy, vitamins, minerals, and low levels of fat. Fruits are high in carbohydrates, vitamins and minerals, and contain virtually no fat—a banana contains 103 calories of energy with 0 grams of fat. Fresh vegetables contain enormous quantities of vitamins, some protein, and almost no fat—a single stalk of broccoli contains 5 grams of protein with no fat, or a single medium-sized potato containing 100 calories has 6 grams of protein and no fat.

Fish, beef, and chicken are loaded with protein,

---

[97]McDonalds Corporation, http://www.mcdonalds.com.

vitamins, minerals, no carbohydrates and widely varying amounts of fat. A 6-ounce serving of fish (halibut) contains 35 grams of protein with 2 grams of fat—versus a 6-ounce steak (rib eye), which contains about the same amount (39 grams) of protein but an incredible 55 grams of fat as well. A 6-ounce serving of chicken (light and dark meat) contains 46 grams of protein with 25 grams of fat.

Unfortunately, we no longer eat as our ancestors did, or even as our parents did. Meals used to be prepared at home primarily using fresh foods and without adding much fat, salt, or chemical preservatives. Today, most of us are too busy to prepare foods from fresh ingredients and purchase foods that are partially—or fully ready to serve—processed with much added fat, sugar, sodium and chemical additives.

The percentage of meals eaten or prepared away from home (restaurants, take-out) has increased more than 50 percent since 1970. Meals prepared outside the home are also much higher in fat and sodium, and lower in vitamins and minerals, than meals prepared at home—even when compared to meals at home made from highly processed foods.[98] Ironically, our biological programming to like the taste of fat—a trait that was responsible for our very survival in prehistoric times—has now become the cause of our worst medical problem.

---

[98]Biing-Hwan Lin, Joanne Guthrie, and Elizabeth Frazao, "Nutrient Contribution of Food Away from Home," *America's Eating Habits: Changes and Consequences*. Edited by Elizabeth Frazao, Food and Rural Economics Division, Economic Research Service, U.S. Department of Agriculture. Agriculture Information Bulletin No. 750 (AIB-750). http://www.ers.usda.gov

Appendix 2

FAT—What Is It, and How Much Is Too Much?

In the Bible the word "fat" is used to describe the most prized parts of the animal—so valuable that they were originally reserved to be burnt at the altar in a sacrifice to God himself. Or, "fat" is used in a figurative sense to describe abundance, exuberance, robustness, fertility or outward success.

In our time the word "fat" has become almost exclusively pejorative—associated with laziness, disgust, slovenliness, greed and gluttony.

But what exactly is fat, and why has it come to have such a negative connotation?

Biologically speaking, fats are a subgroup of a category of nutrients called lipids.

A lipid is the chemical name for a group of compounds that includes fats, oils and cholesterol. A lipid is generally referred to as a fat if it remains solid at room temperature and as an oil if it is liquid at room temperature. Fats and oils come from plant and animal products, whereas cholesterol only comes from animal products such as meat, poultry, milk and cheese.

Cholesterol is an odorless, white, waxy, powdery substance that is found in every cell of our bodies. It is an important building block for cell membranes, hormones and vitamin D, and also aids in the digestion of fat into caloric energy. When doctors talk about "good" and "bad" cholesterol they are actually speaking about lipoproteins.

A lipoprotein is a combination of fat and protein (lipid plus protein) that wraps around the individual fat and cholesterol molecules in our body, transporting them through our bodies and aiding in their digestion. Two major types of lipoproteins are low-density (LDL) lipoproteins and high-density (HDL) lipoproteins. LDL particles, which carry about 70 percent of the cholesterol in our bodies, are known as "bad cholesterol" because they end up depositing cholesterol on the walls of our arteries, which can lead to blockages, strokes and heart attacks. HDL particles are known as "good cholesterol" because they travel through the body picking up cholesterol from dying cells and other sources.

The amount of cholesterol in your system is determined by many factors ranging from your genes to your age to your level of physical activity. For example, smokers have higher cholesterol because smoking weakens the arterial walls and makes the surface membranes more receptive to fat and cholesterol deposits.

But the major determinant of how much bad cholesterol you have is your weight, or more specifically how much excess fat you have in your system.

There are three major types of fats: *polyunsaturated fat, monounsaturated fat* and *saturated fat.* For purposes of simplification, we will refer to the two former types collectively as unsaturated fats.

Basically, saturated fats (e.g., shortening, lard, butter, meat fats) are the chief culprits in raising blood cholesterol—they are naturally "saturated" with hydrogen molecules. Saturated fats are typically solid at room temperature and foods containing saturated fats have a longer shelf life than foods with unsaturated fats.

Unsaturated fats like olive oil and canola oil actually lower blood cholesterol. Unsaturated fats are typically liquid at room temperature but start to solidify when cold—which is why an olive-oil based salad dressing gets cloudy in the refrigerator. Fish contain more unsaturated and less saturated fat than meat—this keeps their bodies from starting to solidify in cold water.

Food manufacturers typically extend the economic shelf life of their products by adding hydrogen to unsaturated fats—a process called hydrogenation—which effectively turns unsaturated fats into saturated fats, or good fats into bad fats called trans-fatty acids. This is why it is important to avoid hydrogenated oils if you are trying to lower your cholesterol.

Fat was prized in biblical times for many reasons. Back then, most humans suffered from a deficiency of fat and basic calories were scarce; being plump was often a sign of great wealth. Fat contains the most energy (9 calories per gram) of any of the six nutrient categories—an important consideration for people choosing to store food either while traveling or for survival between harvests. But probably the main reason fats were so prized then (and now) was because they taste so good.

We are biologically programmed to love eating fat; this programming is now killing us in our world of agricultural abundance. In contrast to times when fat was prized and scarce, today calling someone "fat" is considered a great insult.

But eating fat does not directly make you fat. Eating more calories than you burn makes you fat— or more correctly, makes you overweight. Eating fat indirectly adds to being overweight because fat contains more than twice as many calories per gram as proteins or carbohydrates. And, aside from containing potentially unnecessary calories, eating too much fat is bad because fats contain artery-clogging cholesterol.

When a person becomes overweight, his or her excess fat, as noted earlier, often first appears in the stomach and upper body on a man and on the thighs and lower body in a woman. Upper-body obesity (android obesity) is a male pattern characteristic and is strongly related to heart disease, hypertension and diabetes. It is more dangerous than lower-body obesity (gynecoid obesity), which is a female characteristic but is still dangerous to your health.

But how much fat is too much? In order to answer this question it is first necessary to define the terms "overweight" and "obese." While they are often used interchangeably, *overweight* refers to an excess of total body weight (including all bodily tissues), while *obese* refers to an excess of only body fat. It is possible to be overweight without being obese, as in the case of a body builder with great muscle mass. It is also possible to be obese without being overweight as in the case of a sedentary person with an excess of body fat and low muscle mass.

There are four main methods used today to define being overweight or obese: Percentage Body Fat, Waist-to-Hip ratio, Body Mass Index (BMI) and Height-Weight tables.

The first and most accurate method is to measure the percentage of your body that is fat. Men should have a percentage body fat between 13 and 25 percent and women should have a percentage body fat between 17 and 29 percent. Anything above these numbers is considered obese and is very dangerous.

Percentage Body Fat is best measured by comparing a person's weight to their weight underwater—this works because fat floats and is less dense than body tissue. Unfortunately, this method is too expensive and complicated and is considered primarily a tool for research.[99] Another way is to use special calipers to measure the skinfold thickness of the triceps and other parts of the body—this method

---

[99]In addition to simply weighing underwater and dry, adjustments must be made for the amount of water displaced (Archimedes principle), water temperature, water density, and lung capacity (using helium).

can be quite accurate when done by a trained professional because half of a person's fat is stored just under their skin. Bioelectrical impedance (resistance) can also be used to measure Percentage Body Fat.

The second method used to measure being overweight and/or obese, Waist-to-Hip Ratio, is calculated by dividing the number of inches around the waistline by the circumference around the hips. A person with a 30-inch waist and 40-inch hip circumference would have a Waist-to-Hip Ratio of 0.75. Obesity is defined as anything over 0.8 for a woman and 1.0 for a man. This method is obviously good for diagnosing upper body (android) obesity but can be woefully inaccurate in many cases such as where someone has lower body (gynecoid) obesity.

The third method used to measure being overweight and/or obese, the Body Mass Index or BMI, was developed in 1835 by the French mathematician Adolphe Quetelet. Using a statistical model to develop the concept of the *homme moyen,* or average man, he developed the Quetelet Index, which today is better known as the BMI:

BMI = (weight in kilograms)/(height in meters)^2

Example: A person with a weight of 170 pounds and a height of 5 feet 9 inches would have a BMI of about 25. (170 lbs / 2.2 lb/kg = 77.27 kg, 5.75 ft / 3.28 ft/meter = 1.75 meters, 1.752 = 3.0625, and 77.27 kg / 3.0625 = 25.2 BMI)

Shortcut: Multiply your weight in pounds by 704.5, then divide by your height in inches twice (170 x 704.5) / 69 / 69 = 25.2).

Most countries and public authorities today use BMI as their measurement tool of choice. According to the National Institutes of Health, 61 percent of the U.S. population is overweight (defined as having a BMI of 25 or greater), and almost 27 percent of the U.S. population is obese (defined as having a BMI of

30 or greater).

While these numbers appear to be accurate—just walk outside to a public place and count the percent of people you think look overweight and obese—they are woefully inaccurate when applied to specific individuals. The BMI formula is the same for both sexes; a 5' 9" woman weighing 170 pounds is obviously different than a 5' 9" man weighing the same amount, yet both are considered overweight. The BMI formula is also not adjusted for individual differences, such as whether the person is a weightlifter (i.e., muscle weighs more than fat) or elderly (i.e., lower muscle mass).

And finally, the fourth method, a Height-Weight table, is what people are most familiar with since it has been used by the U.S. medical profession for decades. The popular "Desirable Height-Weight Table" was developed by the Metropolitan Life Insurance Company in 1959 and represents the weight and height statistically associated with the lowest incidence of mortality among their insured population (made up of mostly upper- and middle-class white males). The term "desirable" refers only to having the lowest incidence of mortality, not the lowest incidence of disease, and was removed from the name of the table in 1983. Although the Height-Weight Table is potentially more accurate than BMI, since it is broken down by sex, it has most of the same limitations and should not be considered definitive for any individual circumstance. Additionally, much of the data contained on the current Metropolitan Life Height Weight Table is arbitrary—the concept of frame size (determined by elbow width) was added with no empirical data to support it.

But regardless of which method we choose to determine the percent of our population that is overweight or obese, it is clear that we have a problem of epidemic proportions.

Appendix 3

Highlights from *The Next Trillion*

...on discrimination

In our 21st century we have replaced racial and gender discrimination with a new kind of discrimination based on a person's weight and appearance.

Weight and appearance now define social and economic opportunities just as family name and birth did in the nineteenth century. Whereas in the past poverty was associated with thinness and obesity with wealth, most people who are overweight today occupy the lower rungs of the economic ladder.

Rich fat man has become an oxymoron, and *poor* and *fat* have become synonyms.

More than half the U.S. population is not enjoying this great economy, and this division is not because of their annual income, the color of their skin, their religion, or the place where they were born.

The overweight and obese are widely discriminated against and unjustly accused of entirely creating the problem for themselves.

Every one of us personally knows someone who is not making it today because of his or her weight or health. Imagine how their lives could change if they lost 15 pounds, or found new energy to enjoy their family, or could have the pain they have been told to accept removed from their body.

...on being overweight and unhealthy

61% of the U.S. population is overweight, and 27% are clinically obese—overweight to a point where they are hopeless and have no idea where to turn for help. Both these figures increased 10% from 1994–1999, and obesity has almost doubled since 1980.

Think of this in terms of human suffering—77 million Americans are now clinically obese, and 184 million are overweight.

Each of the 77 million people who are obese represents a life misspent—they don't have the energy to fully enjoy their lives, their work and their families.

The 107 million overweight, but not obese, individuals are often malnourished to the point of fatigue, nervousness, headaches, confusion and muscle weakness. When they turn to their medical community, they are told that these are normal symptoms of advancing age, rather than problems caused by the same poor diet of "empty calories" that causes their extra pounds.

The major reason so many people are unhealthy and obese has more to do with economics than with medicine.

It may be impossible for some people to take control of their weight and their health until they understand the food and medical industries that represent 30% of our national economy.

The overweight and unhealthy spend their lives on a medical merry-go-round that treats a minimal amount of their symptoms—just enough to keep them alive and consuming more unhealthy food and more sickness products and services.

...on health and nutrition

Most people with normal weight are unhealthy, although they often don't know it.

Modern medicine tells us to accept headaches, body pain, fatigue, arthritis and thousands of other common ailments as the inevitable symptoms of aging, yet these ailments are the direct result of having a terrible diet.

When it comes to understanding nutrition, vitamins, minerals and natural supplements and how they prevent disease and affect the aging process, we are only where medical science was two centuries ago when it came to conquering infectious disease: Doctors knew from observations what worked, but were unable to explain why the things worked.

Until recently, most people were told to accept their wellness deficiencies as part of the aging process, as if there was nothing they could do about them.

The human body requires a daily intake of 13 essential vitamins along with certain minerals to sustain the millions of chemical reactions our bodies perform each day. The majority of Americans, however, including many who appear healthy on the outside, are not getting the minimal amount of these vitamins and minerals that their bodies require.

Vitamin deficiencies manifest themselves short-term as a lack of energy, joint pain, failing eyesight, hearing loss and thousands of other ailments that medical science tells us to accept with advancing age. Over the long term these deficiencies cause major illnesses like cancer and heart disease.

It has also been discovered that these same vitamins are able to prevent disease from developing, make us feel even "better than well," and even slow the aging process itself.

Highly effective natural supplements—from gingko to St. John's wort—illuminate the famous Kabbalistic statement: *"God creates the cure before he sends the malady."*

Wherever possible, *you should make your medicine your food and your food your medicine.*

Too many people wait until their health is severely impaired before they take action, or think that they are already fit and healthy—so why should they spend time trying to fix something that is not broken.

We have yet to approach the limits of how strong and healthy we can feel. Improving your health is like climbing mountains—each peak you climb becomes the base from which you ascend to another higher range of mountains, the peaks of which were previously regarded as unreachable.

...on the food industry

A powerful trillion-dollar food industry bombards us with messages calculated to make us eat more and more of the worst possible food. Understanding how the food industry works today is crucial for those seeking to control their diet and their life.

One of the great scandals of the junk-food culture is the extent to which its most enthusiastic promoters personally avoid the very products they are pushing.

Many of the emotional and medical challenges some people face today, from controlling one's temper to depression and cancer, are as much products of these junk-food companies as are frozen pizza and "low-fat" cookies.

Each food company studies its "target market" like rats in a laboratory. No expense is spared. Like a deer caught in the telescopic sight of a hunter at close range, the target never has a chance.

In the case of processed foods, the "target market" often consists largely of people weighing more than 200 pounds and earning less than $20,000 per year.

Big Tobacco is not letting its acquired expertise go to waste—they are purchasing the major brands of addictive processed foods. In early 2001 Philip Morris purchased the most popular children's processed food brands, including Oreo Cookies, Ritz Crackers and Life Savers candies.

...on the medical industry

The nefarious practices of the medical industry make those of the food industry pale by comparison.

Just as obese consumers represent the "target" market to the food companies, physicians represent the "target" market to the medical companies. Patients receive the treatment that is the most profitable for the medical supplier, the health insurance company and the individual physician.

Drug companies spend much more money on marketing than they do on research and development.

Most physicians have become "technology dispensers" for the products and services of the large multinational medical companies.

It is more profitable for medical suppliers today to produce products consumers use for the rest of their lives, rather than to make products that a consumer might use only once. *This means spending research*

*and development funds on products that treat the
symptoms of diseases rather than the causes or the
cures.*

The food and medical companies follow their own
Golden Rule: *He with the gold makes the rules.*

...on the cover-up of the solution

Actors, singers and models consume a pro-vegetarian
diet lacking in processed and addictive fast foods, yet
these societal role models keep their diets to
themselves. They fear being boycotted by a television
industry where most advertising revenue comes from
processed food companies and fast-food restaurants.

Our politicians have been controlled by the food and
drug companies for so long that our government is
now part of the problem rather than poised to be part
of a solution.

Although we've won the Cold War, half of our people
have become personally enslaved—enslaved to a
lifestyle that limits their daily life, dreams and
happiness as much as any authoritative government
or dictatorship.

The companies comprising the U.S. $1 trillion food
industry and the $1.4 trillion medical industry are
governed by universal laws of economics that cause
them to act, in concert, as if they were part of a vast
conspiracy.

...on the dividing of our nation

America has become a *healthocracy*—a two-party
system of "haves" and "have-nots"—divided between
those who successfully manage their health and
those who don't.

But within the 39% of Americans who are not overweight, there are millions of Americans who are healthier than ever before. This group includes the movers and shakers in our society and celebrities who literally make their living on how they look.

This group has quietly embraced a revolutionary new approach—to diet, to exercise, to vitamins, to nutritional supplements, to medical care, and, most important, to the aging process itself.

Movie stars and other entertainment professionals inhabit a secret world in which food, exercise, vitamins, nutritional supplements, medical care and aging are seen from a radically different perspective.

Within this fortunate group, we see the beginnings of a new industry dedicated to wellness that will eventually far surpass the existing healthcare industry we have today that is dedicated to sickness.

...on religion and the wellness industry

The great religions of the world became great by addressing social injustice and the secular needs of their congregants: Today there is no greater social injustice, and no greater secular need, than the need of their congregants to take control of their weight and health.

Gluttony is denounced from Exodus through Jude, and is one of the original seven deadly sins, but gluttony is virtually ignored by most religions today.

The right choices to make on food and health can be traced back to the original teachings of Moses, Jesus, Mohammed and their disciples.

The concept of getting close to God through having a fit and healthy body is evident throughout the Old and New Testaments, but was purged in the Middle Ages as a reaction to the emphasis put on physical appearance by Greek and Roman persecutors.

The wellness-oriented focus on how they will feel later on because of each physical exercise or because of what they are not eating. This makes what seems painful to others become, to them, a euphoric experience with its own immediate rewards.

The wellness-oriented value their healthy diets much as the Orthodox Jew or Muslim values their dietary laws, experiencing in their daily dining a sense of distinction, specialness and closeness to God.

...on the emerging wellness industry

After years of researching the food and medical industries, I can now see an emerging industry in which the greatest fortunes of the next century will be created—fortunes that will eclipse the fortunes of the Internet billionaires of the 1990s.

One-seventh, $1.4 trillion, of the U.S. economy today is devoted to the healthcare business which is really the "Sickness Industry"—defined as "ill health, illness, a disordered, weakened, or unsound condition, or a specific disease."

By the year 2010, an additional $1 trillion of the U.S. economy will be devoted to "wellness industry"— providing healthy people products to make them feel even healthier, look better, slow down the effects of aging, or to prevent diseases from developing in the first place.

No one really wants to be a customer of the sickness industry. Everyone wants to be a customer of the wellness industry.

Most wellness industry sales did not exist only two decades ago. Today they already total approximately $200 billion in annual sales, about half the amount spent on U.S. automobiles.

Baby Boomers are already responsible for the largest stock market rise in history, the housing boom, international airlines, the PC, the Internet, the SUV—in short, about $5 trillion today of our $10 trillion national economy. These boomers are about to spend an additional $1 trillion to preserve what they hold dearest: their youth.

In the next ten years, U.S. baby boomers will increase their spending on wellness-based services from approximately $200 billion today to $1 trillion.

The demand for wellness-based products is primarily driven by the genetic code which causes aging. The understanding and eventual manipulation of this genetic code holds the greatest promise for the wellness industry.

...on the unlimited demand for wellness products

Advancing technology constantly creates its own demand—offering new products that soon become *basic primary needs* for the majority of the population.

Today almost 95% of the things we spend our money on—which most of us think of as *necessities*—were not even around when many of us were born.

When *quantity demand* is satiated, *quality demand* kicks in. When you have all the food, clothing and TVs you need—as most Americans do today—you start wanting better food, better clothing and better TVs.

Almost all new luxury products have one major drawback: They take time to enjoy. Each year consumers get more and more disposable income but less and less time to enjoy it.

Wellness products and services do not take time to enjoy. Money spent to make a person feel stronger, smile better, look younger, or feel healthier yield rewards that are enjoyed on the job, at home and at every moment in between.

Many potential wellness customers have never even heard of wellness products and services, let alone tried them. Medical science has told people to expect and accept declining health and energy levels as they age.

Each satisfied wellness customer is just beginning a lifetime of consumption of products and services that have the potential to improve every aspect of their life.

When consumers see the efficacy of just one wellness industry product, they become voracious customers with an unlimited appetite for more wellness products and services.

Sickness-based health insurance today will be replaced by wellness-based health insurance that will gladly pay for weight reduction, nutritional advice, vitamins, minerals, smoking cessation and hundreds of other wellness-related treatments.

...on the distribution of wellness products and services

In business and technology, changes that used to take place in 50 years or more now take place in 5 years or less.

Throughout history, the only consistent success has come from distributing the ever-expanding production of the latest technology.

The 1967 movie *The Graduate* offered a one-word solution for economic success: "Plastics." In 2001, thanks to "plastics" and so many other better ways of making things, the greatest opportunities now lie in finding better ways to distribute things.

The greatest personal fortunes of the past three decades were made by people who found better ways of distributing things rather than better ways of making things—people like Sam Walton (Wal-Mart), Fred Smith (Federal Express), Ross Perot (EDS), and Jeff Bezos (Amazon.com).

But where Walton, Smith, and Perot found better ways to physically distribute products *that consumers already knew they wanted,* Bezos and the billionaires of the 21st century are making their distribution fortunes educating consumers about new products *that consumers don't even know are available.*

Physical distribution is the process of helping customers physically obtain products that they already know they want. *Intellectual distribution* is the process of educating customers about products that they don't know even exist or don't know are now affordable.

Intellectual vs Physical Distribution is the greatest entrepreneurial opportunity now and for the foreseeable future.

...on direct-selling and the wellness industry

In the 1990s, the most successful vitamin and nutritional supplement products were launched through direct-selling companies—products that were only available through direct one-on-one sales.

Led by nutritional products and new technology, U.S. sales of direct-selling companies rose 50%—from approximately $18 billion in 1995 to $27 billion in 1999. This was almost twice the growth rate of traditional retail stores during a similar time period.

For every household that starts using a better consumer product—from the latest digital camera to educational software to healthier foods and nutritional supplements—there are many more new products and services that consumers haven't yet learned even exist.

Teaching consumers about such products and services *(Intellectual Distribution)*, is the greatest entrepreneurial opportunity now and for the foreseeable future.

Direct selling companies have a long growth curve ahead of them—annual U.S. direct selling sales of approximately $30 billion still amount to less than 1% of the more than $3 trillion ($3,000 billion) in sales at traditional U.S. retail stores.

...on employees and health (sickness) insurance

Today millions of Americans cannot change jobs or quit and strike out on their own because they cannot obtain affordable medical care from anywhere except their current employer.

People receiving health insurance through their employers are actually the most at risk. It is only a question of time before their employer can no longer afford to provide them benefits, or before a member of their family develops a chronic condition that will limit their opportunity to change jobs or find another employer.

Employer-provided health insurance focuses on paying for the treating of the symptoms of illness rather than on preventing illness—almost all expenses to prevent illness (e.g., exercise, vitamins, nutritional supplements) are disallowed for reimbursement.

The U.S. federal tax code allows a tax deduction for the purchase of expensive prescription drugs (like Prozac) but does not allow the same deduction for safer and cheaper nonprescription remedies like St. John's wort. The IRS should not be telling consumers what drugs to take or not to take for their ailments.

...on changes taking place in health insurance

The $1.4 trillion that Americans currently spend on sickness is expected to double by 2010. Its fallout could make the $200 billion savings and loan disaster of the 1980s pale by comparison—tens of millions of Americans could lose their life savings to medical expenses.

Despite a steadily rising economy in the last decade, U.S. personal bankruptcy filings doubled—from approximately 750,000 in 1990 to 1.5 million in 1999—with much of the increase resulting from family medical catastrophes.

There is great opportunity for wellness-oriented individuals to profit from the coming chaos, once they understand how existing health insurance works and how they can structure "wellness insurance" for themselves and their families.

Starting 2001, self-employed individuals may deduct from their taxable income 60% of the amount they spend on health insurance premiums for themselves, their spouses and their dependents. This figure rises to 70% in 2002 and to 100% in 2003 and thereafter.

Congress has extended the opportunity for self-employed Americans to open Medical Savings Accounts (MSAs) until January 31, 2003. Individuals who take advantage of this legislation will be allowed to make tax-deductible contributions to their own sickness and wellness savings account for the rest of their working lives.

MSAs, and other newly-available forms of wellness financing, allow the consumer to make their own intelligent sickness and wellness decisions (like weighing choices like the cost of vitamins and better nutrition today versus the cost of treating a disease later on).

...on paying for wellness (i.e., wellness insurance)

U.S. households, on average, consume $5,000 per annum in medical insurance premiums—but 4/5 of these households incur virtually no medical expenses each year and 1/5 incur $25,000 or more because they or a family member have a preexisting chronic condition.

Individuals in this fortunate 4/5 group can opt out of the employer-sickness insurance marketplace—saving themselves an immediate $3,000 a year and structuring their own wellness-oriented insurance accounts.

By taking advantage of new legislation, individuals can structure "wellness insurance" for themselves combining a high-deductible sickness insurance policy with a Medical or Wellness Savings Account that pays for both sickness and wellness purchases.

Unlike with a corporate group insurance policy, the premium on the sickness component of an individual insurance policy cannot be increased if an insured develops a chronic condition—effectively guaranteeing them and their dependents renewable affordable health insurance for life.

Eventually, beginning with self-employed individuals, most Americans will have a wellness-based insurance system that will pay for weight reduction, nutritional advice, vitamins, minerals, smoking cessation and hundreds of other wellness-related or preventative treatments.

...on eating well and controlling your diet

Our bodies are biologically programmed to seek out foods containing the highest amounts of energy— foods containing the highest amounts of energy (e.g., sugar, fat) taste the best. The exploitation of this biological programming is our major cause of poor health.

While you should always drink at least 8 glasses of water per day, you should try to avoid drinking this water during mealtimes—the chemicals in your stomach become less effective when diluted which can cause valuable nutrients to wash through your body.

We are biologically programmed to eat each meal as if it could be the last one we were going to get for a long time—and in many cases it was before humankind learned how to preserve foods, to farm, and to domesticate animals.

It takes 10-15 minutes from the time we ingest food until our hunger becomes satisfied—this is why you are sometimes no longer hungry at a restaurant when an entrée arrives late. This is also why we often eat too much when we eat quickly at our desk between appointments or at fast-food restaurants.

Our bodily organs replace themselves on a daily to monthly schedule. Without a daily supply of proteins, vitamins and minerals, our bodies and minds deteriorate because we are not able to replace the dying cells in our internal and external organs.

When we don't get enough protein, vitamins and minerals, our initial symptoms include mood swings, fatigue, nervousness, headaches, confusion and muscle weakness. Over the longer term, poor nutrition can cause cancer, hypertension, Alzheimer's disease and many other diseases that we used to just accept as part of our aging process.

Modern medicine typically treats nutritional problems with drugs that focus on each symptom rather than on the underlying problem, which is what we eat, or more correctly in the case of poor nutrition, what we don't eat.

The U.S. food supply is dominated by what nutritional experts call "empty calories"—food containing high amounts of caloric energy but low (or empty) in essential vitamins, minerals and proteins.

Most processed and fast foods contain incredibly high amounts of empty calories, added fat, sodium, and preservatives. In contrast, foods in their natural (unprocessed) state are packed with caloric energy, vitamins, minerals, and low levels of fat.

...on the economic solution to this problem

The overweight and unhealthy among us have become slaves to the combined economic interests of the $1 trillion food industry and the $1.4 trillion sickness industry. But there is an economic solution to this economic problem.

The companies and individuals in the emerging wellness industry carry a message that is far more important than the actual products or services they are trying to sell—that you, individually, can do something about the obesity and ill health that afflicts the majority of our citizens.

It typically takes three affirmative decisions by a consumer before he or she actually tries a new product, and even more exposures to a product and its benefits to get to each affirmative decision. Each message from a wellness supplier brings the consumer one step closer to making an affirmative decision that may change his or her entire life.

Once consumers try a product and have a positive wellness product experience, they typically become voracious consumers of more wellness products and services.

- The single mother who lost 35 pounds now wants to join a fitness club for even more energy.

- The boy with more energy from a new vitamin regimen now wants to learn about better nutrition and change his diet.

- The father who eliminated pain with magnetic therapy now wants to learn about better vitamins.

- The parents of a girl without colds thanks to echinacea now wants to learn what's available for their other children.

- The former athlete using glucosamine who has returned to bicycling now wants something to improve his memory.

- And the prostate patient who was cured with saw palmetto now wants to spread his message about naturopathic experiences.

Each satisfied wellness customer is just beginning a lifetime of consumption of products and services that have the potential to improve every aspect of life for every moment of their life.

Selected Bibliography

Alternative Medicine: The Definitive Guide. Puyallup, WA: Future Medicine Publishing, Inc. 1993.

Anders, George. *Health Against Wealth: HMOs and the Breakdown of Medical Trust.* New York: Houghton Mifflin Company, 1996.

Andrews, Charles. *Profit Fever: The Drive to Corporatize Healthcare and How to Stop it.* Monroe, ME: Common Courage Press, 1995.

Andrews, Sam S., M.D., Luis A. Balart, M.D., Morrison C. Bethea, M.D., and H. Leighton Steward. *Sugar Busters!: Cut Sugar to Trim Fat.* New York: Ballantine Books, 1998.

Bailey, Covert. *The New Fit or Fat.* Boston: Houghton Mifflin Company, 1991.

Balch, James F., M.D., and Phyllis A. Balch, C.N.C. *Prescription for Nutritional Healing.* Garden City Park, NY: Avery Publishing Group Inc., 1990.

Behe, Michael J. *Darwin's Black Box: The Biochemical Challenge to Evolution.* New York: Simon & Schuster, 1998.

Berman, Louis A. *Vegetarianism and the Jewish Tradition.* New York: Ktav Publishing House, Inc., 1982.

Binzel, Phillip E., Jr., M.D. *Alive and Well: One Doctor's Experience with Nutrition in the Treatment of*

Cancer Patients. Westlake Village, CA: American Media, 1994.

Brown, Montague, Everett A. Johnson, Richard L. Johnson. *The Economic Era of Healthcare: A Revolution in Organized Delivery Systems.* San Francisco: Jossey-Bass, Inc., 1996.

Castro, Janice. *The American Way of Health: How Medicine Is Changing and What It Means to You.* New York: Little Brown and Company, 1994.

Dauner, C. Duane, with Michael Bowker. *The Healthcare Solution: Understanding the Crisis and the Cure.* Sacramento, CA: Vision Publishing, 1994.

Diamond, Harvey and Marilyn. *Fit for Life.* New York: Warner Books, Inc., 1985.

Diamond, Harvey and Marilyn. *Fit for Life II: Living Health.* New York: Warner Books, 1989.

Eddy, Mary Baker. *Science and Health with Key to the Scriptures.* Washington, D.C.: Office of the Librarian of Congress, 1934.

Follard, Sherman, Allen C. Goodman, and Miron Stano. *The Economics of Health and Healthcare.* Upper Saddle River, NJ: Prentice-Hall, Inc., 1997.

Fraser, Laura. *Losing It: America's Obsession with Weight and the Industry That Feeds on It.* New York: Penguin Books USA Inc., 1997.

Frech, H.E., III. *Competition and Monopoly in Healthcare.* La Vergne, TN: American Enterprise Press, 1996.

Gaesser, Glenn A. *Big Fat Lies: The Truth About Your Weight and Your Health.* New York: Fawcett Columbine, 1996.

Herzlinger, Regina. *Market Driven Healthcare: Who Wins, Who Loses in the Transformation of America's Largest Service Industry.* Reading, MA: Addison-Wesley Publishing Company, 1997.

Kalechofsky, Roberta, Ph.D. *Vegetarian Judaism: A Guide for Everyone.* Marblehead, MA: Micah Publications, Inc., 1998.

Katahn, Martin, Ph.D. *The T-Factor Diet: Lose Weight Safely and Quickly Without Cutting Calories — or Even Counting Them!* New York: W. W. Norton & Company, Inc., 1989.

Kunnes, Richard M.D. *Your Money or Your Life: Rx for the Medical Market Place.* New York: The Cornwall Press, Inc., 1971.

Millenson, Michael L. *Demanding Medical Excellence: Doctors and Accountability in the Information Age.* Chicago: The University of Chicago Press, 1997.

Morreim, E. Haavi. *Balancing Act: The New Medical Ethics of Medicine's New Economics.* Washington, D.C.: Georgetown University Press, 1995.

Muller, H.G., and G. Tobin. *Nutrition and Food Processing.* Westport, CT: The Avi Publishing Company, Inc., 1980.

Ornish, Dean. *Dr. Dean Ornish's Program for Reversing Heart Disease.* New York: Random House, Inc., 1990.

Osmani, S.R. *Nutrition and Poverty.* New York: Oxford University Press, Inc., 1992.

Pilzer, Paul Zane. *God Wants You To Be Rich: The Theology of Economics.* New York: Simon & Schuster/Fireside, 1995/1997.

Pilzer, Paul Zane. *Unlimited Wealth: The Theory and Practice of Economic Alchemy.* New York: Crown Publishers, 1990/1994.

Pilzer, Paul Zane, with Robert Dietz. *Other People's Money: The Inside Story of the S&L Crisis.* New York: Simon & Schuster, 1989.

Porter, Roy. *The Greatest Benefit to Mankind: A Medical History of Humanity.* New York: W. W. Norton & Company, Inc., 1997.

Powter, Susan. *Stop the Insanity: Change the Way You Look and Feel—Forever.* New York: Simon & Schuster, 1993.

Reid, Daniel P. *The Tao of Health, Sex, and Longevity: A Modern Practical Guide to the Ancient Way.* New York: Fireside, 1989.

Roberts, Marc. J., with Alexandra T. Clyde. *Your Money or Your Life: The Healthcare Crisis Explained.* New York: Doubleday, 1993.

Rodwin, Marc A. *Medicine, Money and Morals: Physicians' Conflicts of Interest.* New York: Oxford University Press, 1993.

Shaouli, Rabbi Moshe Cohen, and Rabbi Yaakov Fisher. *Nature's Wealth: Health and Healing Plants Recommended by Professors of Science and Medicine.*

English Edition Edited by Ruth Steinberg. Copyright Rabbi Jacob Fisher, 1999.

Simon, Julian L. *The State of Humanity.* Cambridge, MA: Blackwell Publishers, Inc., 1995.

Skidelsky, Robert. *John Maynard Keynes: Hopes Betrayed,* 1883–1920. Harmondsworth, Middlesex, England: Penguin Books, 1986.

Skidelsky, Robert. *John Maynard Keynes: The Economist as Savior,* 1920–1937. Harmondsworth, Middlesex, England: Penguin Books, 1994.

Starr, Paul. *The Social Transformation of American Medicine: The Rise of a Sovereign Profession and the Making of a Vast Industry.* Basic Books, 1982.

The PDR Family Guide to Prescription Drugs. New York: Crown Trade Paperbacks, 1996.

Tips, Jack, N.D., Ph.D. *The Pro Vita! Plan: Your Foundation for Optimal Nutrition.* Austin, TX: Apple-A-Day Press, 1993.

Weil, Andrew, M.D. *Eating Well for Optimum Health: The Essential Guide to Food, Diet, and Nutrition.* New York: Alfred A. Knopf, 2000.

Weiss, Lawrence D. *Private Medicine and Public Health: Profit, Politics, and Prejudice in the American Healthcare Enterprise.* Boulder, CO: Westview Press, 1997.

Wyke, Alexandra. *21st-Century Miracle Medicine: RoboSurgery, Wonder Cures, and the Quest for Immortality.* New York: Plenum Press, 1997.

J

Index

Alzheimer's disease, 146
Amazon.com, 65
American Dairy Association, 16
Amway, 74
android obesity, 156, 157
antitrust legislation, 133
arete, 30
Arnold, Thurman, 3, 4
ARPANET, 77
Arthritis and Common Sense (Witkower), 2
AT&T, 134
Babies "R" Us, 68
baby boom (defined), 36
Behe, Michael, 27-28
Beil, Norman, 130-131
Benadryl, 12
beriberi, 55
Bezos, Jeff, 65
Biblical References, 22, 24, 133, 137
    Ecclesiasticus 30:16, 33
    Garden of Eden, 24, 137
    Genesis, Chapter 1, 137
    Job 42:12-17, 128-129
    Proverbs 23:21, 5, 22
    Sarah's burial place, 133
Blue Cross–Blue Shield of Utah, 100
BMI (Body Mass Index), 156, 157, 158
body replacement, 138
building blocks (defined), 137
calories (defined), 139
carbohydrates (defined), 139
catalysts (defined), 138
category-busters (type of stores), 68-70, 73, 75, 80, 99
Celera Corporation, 40
cholesterol (defined), 153

Christianity, 21, 22, 24, 29
Cisco Systems, 78
Claritin, 12
COBRA (Consolidated Omnibus Reconciliation Act), 89, 90, 108
communism, 126, 133
community-rated (defined), 93
CompUSA, 68
Costco Stores, 70, 73
cowpox vaccine, 26
Darwin's Black Box (Behe), 27
DAW (Dispense-As-Written prescriptions), 11
Dayton-Hudson, 67
deductible (insurance), 94
detail person, 10
distribution cost comparison (1967 vs. 2001), 63
DNA, 28, 40, 41
echinacea, 38, 57, 74, 128
EDS, 64
Einstein, Albert, 129-130
Elman, Philip, 2, 3
energy (defined), 137
ephedra, 74
fair trade laws, 110
fats, lipids (defined), 153
FDA (U.S. Food and Drug Administration), 12, 15
Federal Express, 64
fitness clubs, 35, 36
Fonda, Jane, 16
Fortas, Abe, 3
FTC (Federal Trade Commission), 2-4, 9
Funk, Casimir, 24, 55
GDP (Gross Domestic Product), 52, 82
General Theory (Keynes), 44, 126
Generation X, 39
generic drugs, 11
gingko, 25
glucosamine, 57, 128

gluttony, 22, 23, 29, 103, 153
greek civilization, 24, 29, 30
guaranteed-issue (defined), 93
guaranteed-issue (states), 93
gynecoid obesity, 156
Height-Weight table, 156
HIPAA (Health Insurance Portability and
    Accountability Act of 1996), 89-90
HMO (Health Maintenance Organization), 87, 99
Home Depot, 68-70, 99
Hostess Twinkies, 7, 8
How to Eat for a Healthy Heart (Rodale), 1
hydrogenation, 155
Intel, 78
intellectual distributon (defined), 66
Internet, origination of, 76
Interstate Bakeries Corporation, 8
IRS (Internal Revenue Service), 84, 95, 111-112
Islam, 21, 23, 24, 29, 31
Jesus Christ, 21, 22, 24, 29
Judaism, 21, 23, 29, 31
Keynes, John Maynard, 43-45, 53-54, 79, 126
K-Mart, 68
kosher, 23, 29, 30
Lasik surgery, 35
LDL (low-density lipoproteins), 154
Lehigh University, 2
Levi's, 68
lipids, fats (defined), 153
lipoprotein (defined), 153
magnetic therapy, 57, 127
Macy's, 68
Maimonides, Moses, 21, 29
McCarthy, Senator Joseph, 1
McDonald's Corporation, 7, 8, 122, 151
Medicaid (defined), 118
Medicare (defined), 91
Microsoft, 78

minerals (defined), 145
Mohammed, 24
monounsaturated fat (defined), 154
Moses, 24
MSA (Medical Savings Account) (defined), 107
Nabisco, Inc., 8, 9
National Institute of Health, 11, 157
NOW (Negotiable-Order-of-Withdrawal) Accounts, 109
nutrients (defined), 139
obese (defined), 156
Office Max, 99
Oracle, 78
Oreo Cookies, 7, 8
Other People's Money (Pilzer), 134
overweight (defined), 156
oxidation, 56
pasteurization (defined), 149
Percentage Body Fat, 156
Perot, Ross, 64
PetsMart, 68, 99
Philip Morris, Inc., 8, 9
physical distribution (defined), 66
polyunsaturated fat (defined), 154
poverty line (defined), 119
PPO (Preferred Provider Organization), 85, 87, 100, 101, 105, 111
Prentice Hall, 2
prescription drugs, 11-13
Prevention magazine, 1, 4
Procter & Gamble, 7, 68
professionally beautiful, 30
progressive taxation, 44
prostate, 41, 57, 128
proteins (defined), 145
pycnogenol, 74
quality demand (defined), 49
quantity demand (defined), 49

Quetelet Index, 157
Quetelet, Adolphe, 157
rickets, 55
Rodale, J.I., 1-4
  How to Eat for a Healthy Heart, 1
  This Pace Is Not Killing Us, 1
Rogaine, 35, 121
Russell, Cheryl, 38
S&L industry, 134
saturated fat (defined), 154
saw palmetto, 41, 57, 128
scurvy, 54
Sears, 68
Seven (movie), 144
seven deadly sins, 21, 22, 144
Sherman Antitrust Act of 1890, 133
sickness industry (defined), 34
Silverstone, Alicia, 16
Sixteen Tons (song), 81
Smith, Adam, 128
Smith, Fred, 64
snack tax, 135
Socrates, 32
sodium, 145, 150-152
Sony, 68
soy, 16, 38
speed of change, 59
St. John's wort, 25, 84
Target Corporation, 68
Ten Commandments, 21
The Baby Boom (Russell), 38
The Dick Cavett Show, 4
The Graduate, 62
The Picture of Dorian Gray, (Wilde), 39
The Wealth of Nations (Smith), 128
This Pace Is Not Killing Us (Rodale), 1
toolmakers (defined), 78
Toys "R" Us, 68

Travis, Merle, 81
UCLA, 77
UC–Santa Barbara, 77
University of Utah, 77
Unsaturated fats (defined), 154
USA Today, 12
USDA (United States Department of Agriculture), 148
Venter, Craig J., 40
Viagra, 35, 121
vitamins (defined), 145-146
vitamins, discovery of, 24
Vodaphone, 78
Waist-to-Hip ratio, 156
Wal-Mart, 64, 68, 73-76, 78, 79, 110, 122
Walton, Sam, 64, 65, 67, 76
water (as nutrient, defined), 139
Weigh Down Diet, 29
wellness industry (defined), 34
Wellness Savings Account (WSA) (defined), 104
Wilde, Oscar, 39
Witkower Press, 2
WSA (Wellness Savings Account) (defined), 104
zero-marginal physical distribution cost, 71
zero-marginal production cost, 71

Acknowledgments

All these places have their moments
With lovers and friends I still can recall
Some are dead and some are living
In my life I've loved them all

The Beatles, "In My Life" (First Verse)

Just before his death at age 83, former president Richard Nixon was asked about the most important experience of his life. He replied, "Bebe never asked me about the eighteen and a half minutes." Nixon was referring to the missing minutes of Watergate tape recordings that eventually forced his resignation, and how his best friend, Bebe Rebozo, had never once asked him about the most unanswered historical question of his era.

Looking back two decades at the acknowledgments in my previous books, I see some of the most important experiences of my life—the names of the friends who have supported me through the good and the bad times. Some of these include Ed Ames, Michael Ashkin, Norman and Carol Beil, Reed Bilbray, Jerry Coffee, Deborah and Mitch Gaylord, John Grillos, Kenny Griswold, Richard and Kimberly Jaffe, Stephen Jarchow, John and Meg Hauge, Don and Jan Held, Ann Mather, Anthony Meyer, Dr. Stanley Pearle, Tony Robbins, Paula Sepulvado and Caroline Zemmel.

John Hauge especially stands out as the person who first explained to me what now seems so obvious—that all we really have of value are the people we love.

One of the joys of a new book is the new relationships it fosters and the opportunity to work again with old friends. Here are some who come to mind on this project.

There is Karen Risch and Richard Poe, who each helped me organize the original proposal. There is the eminent professor Michael Behe (coincidentally now teaching at my alma mater, Lehigh University), who helped me understand the biology I should have learned in college. There is the visionary Stuart Johnson, who first saw the potential benefits of this research, and who ultimately guided the project to fruition.

There are hundreds of people I've consulted—some of whom include Dr. David Bergman, Brandon Benson, Kendall Cho, Blair Feulmer, Kat Jonsson, Rita and Stanley Kaplan, Michael Kleinman, David Koren, Ken Mabry, Alex Mastoloni, Dr. Mary Parsons, Jim Smith, Bryce Williams, Gregg Wurster, Karen Wynn, Dexter Yager, Doyle Yager and Steve Yager.

There is the LA-based trainer Lisa Goldenthal, also known as the "sculptor" to her celebrity clientele; Lisa began as my trainer but ended up a close family friend.

There is my researcher Joey D'Allesandro, who has also transitioned from employee to close friend, and my former researcher, Brandon Williams, who planted many of the theological seeds that continue to sprout in my work.

There is my business partner Anthony Meyer, and my CEO Reed Bilbray, who since the 1980s have both selflessly allowed me to shine by their achievements.

There are my former editors Allan Mayer *(Other People's Money),* Jim Wade *(Unlimited Wealth),* and Bob Asahina *(God Wants You To Be Rich)*—all of whom have taught me so much. I'm especially grateful to Jim Wade, who dropped everything on short notice when I needed his help on this manuscript.

There is my literary agent, Ms. Jan Miller, about

whom I can only say what I've said several times before: Jan is commonly known as "the dreammaker" to the many authors, including me, on whom she was the first one to take a chance. Now, after twenty years together, Jan's original role as just my trusted agent has taken a backseat to her role as my cherished friend.

After twenty consecutive years teaching college students at New York University, I now teach Sunday school to teenagers in my local community. Looking back at NYU, I am grateful to the thousands of students who helped me find my main purpose in life: to teach. And I am equally grateful for the close friendships that developed from teaching with outstanding colleagues like George Stone and Morris Sutton.

My last book, *God Wants You To Be Rich* (1995/1997), was dedicated to my most important mentor, Charles Jay Pilzer. Since that dedication, I had the honor of officiating at Uncle Charlie's fiftieth wedding anniversary, where the real star was his wife Geraldine. Aunt Gerry, a model for health and fitness, added as much to this project as her husband has added to my previous works.

And as always, there are my brothers, Stephen and Lee, and their wives, Donna and Meryn. There are my in-laws, Linda and Kieu Dang, and my brother-in-law, Brian Dang—Kieu's pharmaceutical and international background was a great asset in my research. And of course, my mother, Miriam, and my father, Elias, to whom no amount of praise could do justice.

But, going forward, all of this pales by comparison to the gratitude I feel to my wife, Lisa, a former biochemist who stayed up many nights editing my manuscript, and to our new daughter, Miriam. To both of you, I humbly borrow these immortal words of John Lennon:

Though I know I'll never lose affection
For people and things that went before
I know I'll often stop and think about them
In my life I love you more

The Beatles, "In My Life" (Second Verse)

Praise for Professor Pilzer

"Paul Zane Pilzer's unique gift is to tame the mysteries of making money and put you in the saddle. *God Wants You To Be Rich* will set your mind racing with new ideas."
— Scott DeGarmo, Former Editor-in-Chief, Publisher,
Success Magazine

"[*Unlimited Wealth*] A must-read—Paul Zane Pilzer has helped to shift our thinking from scarcity in resources to one of a cornucopia of economic abundance and richness."
— Anthony Robbins, Bestselling author,
Awaken the Giant Within

"In *God Wants You To Be Rich,* bestselling author Paul Zane Pilzer provides an original, provocative view of how to accumulate wealth and why it is beneficial to all of humankind. A theology of economics, this book explores why God wants each of us to be rich in every way—physically, emotionally and financially—and shows the way to prosperity, well-being and peace of mind."
"A challenging yet witty view of who's really in charge of all abundance."
— *Boston Herald*

"Paul Zane Pilzer's *God Wants You To Be Rich* makes you understand how and why the world will be getting ever richer materially. He gets it right."
¬Julian Simon, Professor of Business Administration, University of Maryland, Author of *The Ultimate Resource*

"I'm amazed at your business capacity and, as well, your ability to put into laymen's terms the alchemic process. I know [*Unlimited Wealth*] will be well received and a huge success."
— Sam Walton, Chairman, *Wal-Mart Stores, Inc.*

Praise for Professor Pilzer (cont'd)

"His theory is crystal clear and applicable to anyone....*Unlimited Wealth* is bound to revolutionize the way we view the nation's economy, if not our own lives. Pilzer challenges us to scrap not only the way we think about our daily affairs but the way we prepare ourselves for the future."

– Newark Star Ledger

"Pilzer and *Unlimited Wealth* can give you the equivalent of a college education in just a few hours. He explains not only where the greatest economic opportunities lie today, but what you can do to take advantage of them."

– Dexter Yager, Yager Enterprises, Inc.

"...[*Unlimited Wealth*] explains how today's billionaires will create their wealth by producing goods and services that did not exist at the time of their birth...a good theory that has implicitly become part of modern economic thinking."

– National Review

"*Unlimited Wealth* is as refreshing as a tulip in April. Paul Zane Pilzer has compiled some of the intellectual building blocks that hold expansion theories together...things often lost in the daily exchange of news and information."

– Detroit Free Press

"There is much to like in *Unlimited Wealth*. Pilzer's arguments are refreshingly unrooted in any single ideological camp."

– Washington Monthly

About the Author

Paul Zane Pilzer is a world-renowned economist, a multimillionaire software entrepreneur, a part-time rabbi, a college professor and the author of three bestselling books.

Pilzer completed college in three years and received his MBA from Wharton in fifteen months at age 22. At age 24, he was appointed adjunct professor at New York University, where he taught for twenty consecutive years. While employed as Citibank's youngest officer at age 22 and its youngest vice president at age 25, Pilzer started several entrepreneurial businesses—earning his first $1 million before age 26 and his first $10 million before age 30. Over the past twenty years, Pilzer has started and/or taken public more than five companies in the areas of software, education and financial services.

He was an appointed economic advisor in two presidential administrations and warned of the impending $200-billion savings and loan crisis years before official Washington was willing to listen—a story that he later told in *Other People's Money* (Simon & Schuster, 1989) which was critically acclaimed by *The New York Times* and *The Economist* magazine.

Pilzer's *Unlimited Wealth* (Crown Publishers, 1990/1994) explained how we live in a world of unlimited physical resources because of rapidly advancing technology. After reading *Unlimited Wealth,* the late Sam Walton, founder of Wal-Mart, said that he was "amazed at Pilzer's business capacity" and his "ability to put it into layman's terms."

About the Author *(cont'd)*

Pilzer's *God Wants You To Be Rich* (Simon & Schuster, 1995/1997) explained how the foundation of our economic system is based on our Judeo-Christian heritage. This *New York Times* business bestseller was featured on the front page of *The Wall Street Journal* and on television shows ranging from *60 Minutes* to *First Person with Maria Shriver.* It has been published in 18 languages.

And now, in *The Next Trillion* (VideoPlus, 2001), Pilzer exposes our trillion-dollar food and medical industries and identifies a newly emerging "wellness" industry that will soon occupy an additional one-seventh, or "next trillion," of our economy—an industry in which the fortunes of the new millennium will be created.

Pilzer, a former commentator on National Public Radio and CNN, has appeared three times on the *Larry King Live!* television program and on the cover of several national magazines. He speaks live each year to approximately 500,000 people, and more than 10 million audio and video copies of his speeches have been sold.

He lives in Utah with his wife and children where they are avid snowboarders, mountain bikers and chess players.

The Next Trillion

In *The Next Trillion,* Pilzer exposes the truth about why half the U.S. population is unhealthy and overweight: Americans have become caught between the economic interests of the trillion-dollar food industry and the trillion-dollar healthcare or "sickness" industry.

In analyzing these two gigantic industrial complexes, Pilzer focuses on an emerging "wellness" industry that will soon occupy an additional one-seventh, or "next trillion," of the economy—an industry ripe with entrepreneurial opportunities that will eclipse those of today's Internet-based companies.

Pilzer explains in *The Next Trillion* why consumers will turn away from consuming more material goods and instead seek to achieve internal self-improvement— healthier foods, vitamins, nutritional supplements and fitness programs—and why consumers will create a virtually limitless and sustained demand for wellness-based products.

Many of the products that will take this new industry from a few billion dollars to a few trillion are still in the laboratory. Yet, as Pilzer explains, the greatest entrepreneurial opportunities will be in distributing rather than in manufacturing wellness products and services.

Pilzer shows why the crash of our healthcare insurance system is imminent and why those feeling the most secure—individuals who receive health insurance through their employers—are the most at risk. Here Pilzer recommends specific strategies for wellness-oriented individuals to navigate the icy waters ahead.

The Next Trillion is for businesspeople and consumers wanting to control where one-seventh of their earnings go every year. It is important for anyone who's ever tried to control their weight or maximize their health, or for anyone working in today's healthcare industry. And it is a critical must-read for entrepreneurs who want to know where the greatest opportunities lie ahead in the next two decades.

Above all, *The Next Trillion* offers an exhilarating vision of health and fitness—true wellness that is far more than skin deep.